Making Sense
of Idioms

Making Sense of Idioms

Jake Allsop
and Louise Woods

CASSELL

CASSELL PUBLISHERS LIMITED
Villiers House, 41/47 Strand
London WC2N 5JE

First published 1990

British Library Cataloguing in Publication Data
Allsop, Jake
  Making sense of idioms: self study edition.
  1. English usage. Usage
  I. Title   II. Woods, Louise
  428
  ISBN 0 304 33000 0

British Library Cataloguing in Publication Data
Allsop, Jake
  Making sense of idioms.
  1. English usage. Usage
  I. Title   II. Woods, Louise
  428
  ISBN 0 304 31755 1

Illustrations by Harry Venning
Design by Colin Reed
Typeset by Fakenham Photosetting Limited, Fakenham, Norfolk
Printed in Great Britain by The Bath Press, Avon

Contents

Introduction

How many times have you heard an English expression as simple
as 'Let's call it a day' or as colourful as 'It sticks out like a sore
thumb' and wondered why you can't sound as natural as that?
Students of English often feel awkward when they try to use
idioms as they will sometimes misunderstand the use of the
idiom in the situation or use an idiom that is inappropriate.
Idioms in English are basic to the language and yet they are the
most difficult part of it to learn.

In this book we have taken about 200 or so common idioms and
group them into functional areas where they would naturally
occur. We have also included an alphabetical reference section
which gives more explanation and examples of the idioms used.
Sometimes it is enough just to recognise the idiom so you will
understand it when you hear it. Other everyday phrases you will
be able to add to your active knowledge and gradually build up a
store of useful colloquial expressions.

Jake Allsop
Louise Woods

1 Loving and hating

Expressions	
liking **to think the world of someone**	disliking **to have no time for someone**
loving **to be head over heels in love with someone**	hating **not to be able to stand the sight of someone/ something**

I   Make sentences for each pair of pictures using the expressions above. We have done the first one to help you.

Is she a good mother to her children?

I   Yes, she ___*thinks the*___   2   No, she _____
___*world of them.*___

Is Bill very fond of Julia?

3   Yes. In fact he _____   4   No. In fact he _____

_____   _____

2   Replace the underlined words with an expression based on the word(s) given in brackets. We have done the first one to help you.

5   When I was young, I was <u>crazy about</u> the girl next door. (*heels*)

I was head over heels in love with the girl next door.

6   I <u>really hate to see</u> good food going to waste. (*stand/sight*)

_____

7   Most of us <u>are against</u> people who drink and drive. (*no time*)

_____

8   Our teacher <u>says that we are wonderful.</u> (*world*)

_____

3   You might hear the idiomatic expressions which are underlined in these sentences. Which ones are about **loving/liking** (circle A) and which are about **hating/disliking** (circle B)? We have done the first one for you.

9 The sound of insects buzzing <u>gets on my nerves</u>.	A Ⓑ
10 Julia <u>has a crush on</u> her teacher, which is very embarrassing for everyone.	A B
11 The noise of a fly buzzing round me when I am trying to sleep really <u>drives me up the wall</u>.	A B
12 I think that boy over there has really <u>taken a fancy to</u> you, Julia!	A B
13 I'm <u>sick and tired of</u> being told to keep my room tidy.	A B
14 John was <u>thrilled to bits</u> when he heard that his brother was getting married.	A B

4   Use the expressions underlined in Exercise 3 to comment on these situations. We have suggested comments for the first one to help you.

15 Every day my mother criticises my clothes, my hair, and everything I do.

It / She drives me up the wall.

16 Can you imagine how I felt when I heard that I had won first prize in the national lottery?

_____

17 My neighbour plays the trumpet for three hours every night, and I can hear every note.

_____

18 You see something in a shop window and you would really like to have it.

_____

19 A girl of fifteen believes she is in love with her piano teacher.

_____

5 **Review**

Fill in the missing words in this text.

20 I know that my boyfriend, George, _____ the world _____ me. We fell head

_____ _____ _____ love the first time we saw each other. My friends said

that I had a _____ _____ him, and that it wasn't true love, but I have _____

time _____ people who laugh at young love. I'm _____ and _____ of people

telling me 'You're too young to be in love'. They really _____ _____ my nerves. It

_____ me _____ _____ wall the way they always think they know best.

Anyway, I was _____ to bits when George asked me to go out with him, and I know

that this is the real thing and not just an adolescent fancy.

2 Getting angry and not getting angry; believing and not believing

Expressions	
getting angry	not getting angry
to lose your temper	**not to say a word**
believing	not believing
not to put it past someone	**not to believe a word of it**

I   Make sentences for each pair of pictures using the expressions above.

Was your father angry when you came home late last night?

I Yes, he _____   2 No, he _____

_____   _____

They say John cheated in the examination. Do you think he would do such a thing?

3 Yes, I wouldn't _____   **4** No, I _____

_____   _____

2   Replace the underlined words with an expression based on the word given in brackets.

5 My sister is usually very quick-tempered, but she <u>just remained silent</u> when I took her best shoes without asking. (*word*)

_____

6 People are saying that the Council intends to pull down the Town Hall, but I <u>feel sure that it is untrue</u>. (*word*)

_____

7 Well, <u>I think the Council is capable of doing</u> something crazy like that. (*past*)

_____

8 Try not to <u>get angry</u>: you know it's bad for your blood pressure. (*temper*)

_____

3   You might hear the idiomatic expressions which are underlined in these sentences. Which ones are about **getting angry** (circle A) and which ones are about **not getting angry** (circle B)?

9 The children love to pull the dog's tail and ears, but the dog <u>doesn't take any notice</u>.	A B
10 Our teacher rarely <u>flies off the handle</u>, but when she does, we all keep out of her way.	A B
11 My mother really <u>hit the roof</u> when she found out that I had crashed the car.	A B
12 My parents <u>didn't bat an eyelid</u> when I announced that I was going to become a nun.	A B

You might hear the idiomatic expressions which are underlined in these sentences. Which ones are about **believing** (circle A) and which ones are about **not believing** (circle B)?

13 A: John says he can hold his breath for five minutes. B: <u>A likely story</u>!	A B
14 A: They say Mrs Brown stole £200 from work. B: Well, <u>there's no smoke without fire</u>.	A B
A: You may be right, but <u>I doubt if there's anything in it</u>.	A B
15 A: I've heard you can earn $50,000 a year as a secretary in America. B: I'd <u>take that with a pinch of salt</u> if I were you.	A B
16 I <u>couldn't believe my ears</u> when they told me my uncle was a Russian spy.	A B

4   Use expressions underlined in Exercise 3 to comment on these situations.

17 You have heard that school holidays will be increased by 50%.

_____

18 Everyone knows that Sally tells lies. One day, she told you that her father was a millionaire.

_____

19 The boss was very displeased when he saw how many spelling mistakes there were in the Report.

_____

20 A child asked his father for £2000, expecting his father to be either angry or surprised, or both. In fact, his father didn't react at all: he just gave his son the money.

_____

21 Yesterday you saw an amazing sight: a car with six clowns on top of it going down the High Street.

_____

5   Review

Fill in the missing words in these texts.

22 My parents didn't _____ _____ eyelid when I told them I wanted to work in India as a missionary. In fact, my father, instead of _____ the roof as I expected him to, didn't _____ a word. He just smiled. My mother, who easily _____ _____ temper, also remained calm. In fact, after some discussion, they even offered to pay my air fare: I _____ _____ _____ ears!

23 A lot of people say that my brother is a liar. Well, I admit he tends to exaggerate, and you have to _____ everything he says with a _____ of _____, but he doesn't really mean to mislead people. But the problem is that people no longer _____ _____ word he says. Of course I wouldn't _____ _____ _____ him to tell lies if he needed to, but it's a pity he has such a bad name, especially as he is a Member of Parliament.

3 Being safe and taking risks

1 Make sentences for each pair of pictures using the expressions above.

I hear the new boss is very bad tempered.

1 Yes, you have to _____

_____

Rob has bet £500 on that old horse.

2 He's really _____

_____

What has Arturo done to his house?

3 Well, he likes _____

_____

Has Caroline finally gone to live in Alaska?

4 Yes, she decided to _____

_____

2   Replace the underlined words with an expression based on the word given in brackets.

5 Sometimes you have to <u>do something you're not sure about</u>. (*neck*)

_____

6 If you want to succeed in this job, you must always <u>be careful</u>. (*step*)

_____

7 My mother never takes chances. She likes to <u>be sure of everything</u>. (*safe*)

_____

8 Beryl had never flown and was terrified of flying. But when she realised her mother was ill in Australia, she <u>bought a plane ticket</u>. (*plunge*)

_____

3   You might hear the idiomatic expressions which are underlined in these sentences. Which ones are about **being safe** (circle A) and which ones are about **taking risks** (circle B)?

9 Bob's really <u>skating on thin ice</u> talking to that girl. Her husband is very jealous and here he comes!   **A   B**

10 I always get a taxi home at night – <u>it's better to be safe than sorry</u>.   **A   B**

11 I didn't like the look of him so I decided to <u>play it safe</u> and not accept a lift home in his car.   **A   B**

12 He realised he was <u>running a risk</u> putting all his money into a new business.   **A   B**

13 Whenever Mike meets a new girl he always <u>jumps in with both feet</u>, buys her flowers, takes her to dinner and asks her to marry him.   **A   B**

14 Saying 'No' to anything dangerous is always <u>a safe bet</u>, but it doesn't make life very exciting.   **A   B**

4   Use expressions underlined in Exercise 3 to comment on these situations.

15 Mr and Mrs Owen went to the same caravan for their holiday for 35 years.

_____

16 Joyce was stupid to touch that dog. She knew it was dangerous.

_____

17 Keith was asking for trouble when he told his boss what he thought of him.

_____

18 I'm sure the supermarket will still be open. It's only six o'clock.

_____

19 Some people don't think of the consequences when they do something.

_____

20 Other people are more careful in case something goes wrong.

_____

5   **Review**

Fill in the missing words in this text.

21 My two sisters are complete opposites. Mary's very careful about everything. In any

situation she likes to be _____ _____ _____ _____. Emily, on the other

hand, always _____ _____ _____ _____ _____ before she knows all

the possible problems she may meet. When we all wanted to go on holiday together last

year, Mary thought a nice hotel in Spain would be _____ _____ _____, but of

course Emily wanted to hitch-hike to India. I didn't like the idea of hitch-hiking – it seemed

like _____ _____ _____ but I didn't want to _____ _____ _____

with Mary in her nice hotel. In the end we did the only thing possible – we all went away

separately!

4 Making comparisons which emphasise or exaggerate

Adjective	X + Adjective
hungry	starving hungry
wet	soaking wet
sharp	razor sharp

X always means very or completely, ie if you are starving hungry, you are very very hungry and if you are soaking wet, you are very very wet.

X can also be a noun as in razor sharp, ie as sharp as a razor.

I Which one is **wet** and which one is **soaking wet**?

1 _____   2 _____

Which one is **hungry** and which one is **starving hungry**?

3 _____   4 _____

2 Match the adjectives in column B
with a noun from column A.
We have done one for you.

	A	B
5	blood	blue
6	brand	clear
7	crystal	cheap
8	dirt	cold
9	ice	deaf
10	pea or sea	hard
11	razor	green
12	rock	new
13	sky	red
14	snow	sharp
15	stone	thin
16	wafer	white

3 Choose a phrase to complete the sentences. We have done the first one to help you.

bone idle	bolt upright	dead straight	dog tired	piping hot
pitch black	soaking wet	stark naked	. stark staring mad	stone cold sober

17 It's _pitch black_ in here. I can't see a thing. Please switch the light on.

18 The food was _____ _____ when it first came out of the oven.

19 We had to walk home in the rain, so it was not surprising that we were _____ _____
by the time we got home.

20 John is _____ _____. He is too lazy even to tie his own shoelaces.

21 The crowd waved and cheered as she took off all her clothes and ran _____ _____
on to the football pitch.

22 Later, when she realised what a crazy thing she had done, she said to a reporter: 'I must

have been _____ _____ _____ to do such a thing!'

23 It can't have been George who was singing and dancing all night – he was _____

_____ _____.

24 It took us sixteen hours of non-stop work to pick the rest of the grapes, so we were all

_____ _____ at the end of it.

25 The road across the savannah runs _____ _____ for three hundred kilometres – not a curve or bend anywhere.

26 The incredible news of William's death made everyone sit _____ _____ in their seats.

4 Review

Match the cartoons and the captions.

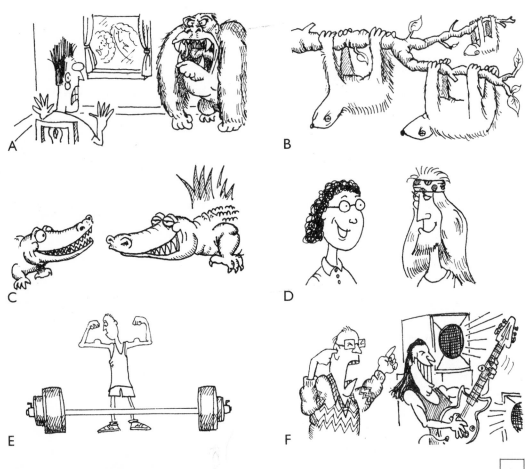

A

B

C

D

E

F

27 And if you're good, I'll buy you a brand new toothbrush for your birthday.

28 If I keep at it, I'll have rock hard muscles one day.

29 You'll be stone deaf by the time you're twenty.

30 Of course, the whole family is bone idle.

31 Why is she sitting bolt upright?

32 I wish my hair was dead straight like yours.

5 Keeping things quiet and not keeping things quiet

Expressions	
keeping things quiet	not keeping things quiet
not to breathe a word	**to let the cat out of the bag**
to keep something to yourself	**to give the game away**

I Make sentences for each pair of pictures using the expressions above.

Did he tell anybody about what happened?

I No, he _____

_____

2 Yes, I'm afraid he _____

_____

Can you trust her not to say anything?

3 Oh yes, I'm sure she _____

_____

4 No, she's sure _____

_____

2   Replace the underlined words with an expression based on the word given in brackets.

5   You can trust John: he will never <u>reveal a secret</u>. (*game*)

_____

6   Now, please <u>don't tell anyone I told you</u>, but . . . (*yourself*)

_____

7   'Who informed the Headmistress that we had been cheating?'

'Not me! I didn't <u>say anything to anybody</u>.' (*word*)

_____

8   I thought we were going to keep our engagement a secret, but everyone guessed the

truth when <u>you mentioned how much you paid for the ring</u>. (*cat*)

_____

3   You might hear the idiomatic expressions which are underlined in these sentences.
Which ones are about **keeping things quiet** (circle A) and which ones are about **not
keeping things quiet** (circle B)?

9   Some managers like to keep their workforce informed about the company's
plans, but others prefer to <u>play their cards close to their chest</u>.   A   B

10 'My life,' said Mrs Kenilworth, 'is <u>an open book</u>.' 'The trouble is,' replied Mr
Kenilworth, 'that it isn't worth reading.'   A   B

11 If I tell you something about Mrs Brown, do you promise to <u>keep it under
your hat</u>?   A   B

12 Any item of news that you tell my brother is sure to <u>spread like wildfire</u>.   A   B

13 Simon is <u>a dark horse</u>: you never know what he's up to.   A   B

14 We're planning a surprise for father's birthday. Please don't <u>give the show
away</u>.   A   B

4   Use expressions underlined in Exercise 3 to comment on these situations.

15 How a person who had nothing to hide might describe himself/herself.

_____

16 The man next door was a very mysterious person. He seemed to be very poor, but
when he died, we discovered that he had left a million pounds in his Will.

_____

17 On Monday morning, the postman told Mrs Smith he had cancer. By lunchtime the same day, everyone in the village knew about it.

_____

18 Joe seems to be a friendly and open person, but in fact he never tells anyone what he is really thinking or planning to do next.

_____

19 We wanted the present to be a surprise for our teacher, but as usual Maria opened her big mouth!

_____

20 The boss asked me not to tell anyone about the salary increase.

_____

5　**Review**

What is the expression that corresponds to each of these pictures? We have done the first one to help you.

21 _not to breathe a word_   22 _____   23 _____   24 _____

25 _____   26 _____   27 _____

Now, write sentences using each expression to show that you know their meaning.

28 _____

29 _____

30 _____

31 _____

32 _____

33 _____

34 _____

6 Describing certainty and impossibility

Expressions	
likely	unlikely
to be on the cards	**to be a long shot**
certain	impossible
to be a sure thing	**to be out of the question**

1 Make captions for each picture using the expressions above.

Do you think we'll have a test today?

1 Yes, I think it's _____

_____

Can I bring my pet into the house?

2 No, I'm afraid _____

_____

Will Simon get that job he wants?

3 Yes, it's _____

_____

Has your dog any chance of winning the race?

4 No, it's _____

_____

2   Replace the underlined words with an expression based on the word(s) given in brackets.

5 I want to buy that new sports car, but on my salary <u>it's quite impossible</u>. (*question*)

_____

6 My boss has told me my promotion <u>is definite</u>. (*thing*)

_____

7 Tom's hoping to qualify for the Olympics swimming team, but at his age, <u>I don't think he has much hope</u>. (*shot*)

_____

8 They say rain <u>is expected</u> for the next few days. (*cards*)

_____

3   You might hear the idiomatic expressions which are underlined in these sentences. Which ones are about being **likely/certain** (circle A) and which ones are about being **unlikely/impossible** (circle B)?

9 I'm going to marry you and <u>there are no two ways about it</u>.   A   B

10 We'd planned to go abroad for six months, but with Jenny's new job <u>it's all very much in the air</u>.   A   B

11 Mary's the finest dancer I've ever seen – <u>there's no question about it</u>.   A   B

12 Terry says he is going to make a million pounds by next year, but personally, <u>I wouldn't bet on it</u>.   A   B

13 Am I going to win that race? <u>You bet!</u>   A   B

14 John tried to put out the fire, but <u>he didn't have a cat in Hell's chance</u> with no water.   A   B

4   Use the expressions underlined in Exercise 3 to comment on these situations.

15 Sarah is definitely the prettiest girl I know.

_____

16 I don't really know where I'll live if and when I get this new job.

_____

17 I certainly will not lend you £500.

_____

18 I don't honestly think you'll pass this exam.

_____

19 I know I definitely won't pass this exam.

_____

5   Review

Fill in the missing words in this text.

20 When Barry went for an interview for a Manager's job, he thought he didn't have a

_____ _____ _____ _____. His workmates told him that at 23 it was

completely _____ _____ _____ _____. 'It may be a _____ _____,'

he thought, 'but I'll try anyway!' At the interview, his boss said that his work was good and

that a promotion was _____ _____ _____. Would he consider a Manager's

job? '_____ _____' said Barry. His workmates changed their ideas immediately.

'We always knew it was a _____ _____.'

7 Praising and criticising; right and wrong

Expressions	
praising	criticising
to give somebody a pat on the back	**to give someone a piece of your mind**
always right	to do something wrong
never to put a foot wrong	**to put your foot in it**

1 Make sentences for each picture using the expressions above.

Did Tony tell you he'd smashed up your car?

1 Yes, he did, and I _____

Julie's the teacher's favourite, isn't she?

2 Yes, she _____

Tony didn't realise that woman was his new boss.

3 No, he really _____

The village really welcomed the winner home.

4 Yes, they all wanted _____

2   Replace the underlined words with an expression based on the word given in brackets.

    5   My parents think my little sister is perfect – she never <u>gets into trouble</u>. (*wrong*)

    _____

    6   They <u>told Bill he was wonderful</u> when he rescued the dog from the river. (*pat*)

    _____

    7   <u>I made a terrible mistake</u> when I told him I didn't like the books. I didn't know he was the author. (*foot*)

    _____

    8   When I told Jeremy I'd lost his favourite cassette, he <u>told me what he thought of me</u>. (*mind*)

    _____

3   You might hear the idiomatic expressions which are underlined in these sentences. Which ones are about **praising/being right** (circle A) and which ones about **criticising/ being wrong** (circle B)?

    9   Don't <u>have a go at him</u>: it's not his fault.   A   B
    10 Whatever that singer did, <u>she couldn't do a thing wrong</u>. She made millions.   A   B
    11 I'm in <u>John's bad books</u> for scratching his new car.   A   B
    12 If you're late once more this week, <u>you'll really be told off</u>.   A   B
    13 He's really in <u>my good books</u> for helping me so much with the garden.   A   B
    14 Whatever I do, he complains. <u>I can't do a thing right</u>.   A   B

4   Use the expressions underlined in Exercise 3 to comment on these situations.

    15 He really tries to please her, but she never likes what he does.

    _____

    16 Anita had nothing but success all her life.

    _____

    17 I'm very pleased with you today, William.

    _____

    18 Say something to that child, Bill – he's stealing the flowers.

    _____

19 Shirley won't talk to Patrick because he's taken her bicycle.

_____

20 Don't shout at me! It's not my fault!

_____

Review

5   Fill in the missing words in this text.

21 All his life my brother Edward had always been in trouble and couldn't _____

_____ _____ _____. Teachers _____ _____ _____ for being late,

for being early, for not being there at all; neighbours _____ him _____ _____

_____ _____ _____ when he played in their gardens and broke their flowers.

He was _____ mother's _____ _____ because he broke all her favourite

vases yesterday. But from now on Edward is a star and _____ _____ _____

_____ _____. The local TV company has just given him the main part in a new

children's TV series and now all the teachers, neighbours and family are giving him a big

_____ _____ _____ _____. Strange how a little horror can suddenly be

_____ everyone's _____ _____!

8 Making comparisons about states

To emphasise a state, we often use the pattern *to be like* X. ie, something is or we are in a similar state to X. For example, if someone is very very pleased, we might say *He is like a dog with two tails* (remember that dogs wag their tails when they are pleased).

Expressions	Meaning
like a bear with a sore head	in a bad mood
like a cat on hot bricks	excited/impatient
like looking for a needle in a haystack	impossible to find
like a red rag to a bull	causing anger

I Complete the captions to these pictures using one of the expressions from the list above.

I suppose Betty really wants to find out what she's getting for her birthday.

I Yes, she's _____

_____

Does Uncle George get very upset when people talk about socialism?

2 Absolutely! Talking about socialism is ___

_____

Do you think you'll find your golf ball in there?

3 I don't think so ... it's like _____

_____

Is he cheerful first thing in the morning?

4 Not at all! He _____

_____

2   Replace the underlined words with one of the above expressions based on the word given in brackets.

5 A: Have you found that receipt I asked you for?
   B: Look, we have at least twenty-five files to go through. <u>It's going to be very difficult to locate one receipt amongst so many</u>. (*needle*)

   _____

6 A: Is this a good time to ask our teacher for the afternoon off?
   B: I wouldn't if I were you. He seems to <u>be in a very bad temper</u> at the moment. (*sore*)

   _____

7 A: What's the matter with Kate? She seems <u>unable to sit still</u> at the moment. (*hot*)

   _____

   B: That's because she's waiting for her examination results.

8 A: Don't mention to the boss that you are a member of a trade union. <u>It makes him extremely annoyed</u>. (*rag*)

   _____

   B: Well, that's *his* problem, isn't it?

3   You might hear the idiomatic expressions which are underlined in these sentences. Study each sentence and then choose the correct meaning from the definitions which follow it.

9 Trying to persuade my uncle to give money to charity is <u>like getting blood out of a stone</u>! My uncle is (**a**) generous (**b**) mean (**c**) difficult to please (**d**) deaf.

10 All the actors said that they had not had enough time to rehearse the play, but in fact everything <u>went like clockwork</u> on the night.
   Everything (**a**) went very badly (**b**) was very mechanical (**c**) went very well (**d**) was late.

11 He looks <u>like nothing on earth</u>! What's the matter with him?
   He (**a**) is clearly very poor (**b**) is ugly (**c**) is staring rudely at everybody (**d**) seems to be ill.

12 You cannot tell her anything: it's <u>like water off a duck's back</u>.
   She (**a**) is deaf (**b**) doesn't enjoy conversation (**c**) is a very rude person (**d**) ignores criticism.

4   Use the expressions underlined in Exercise 3 to comment on these situations.

13   You meet your friend in the street. His eyes are bloodshot, his hair is untidy, his face is very white.

_____

14   The teacher gets very angry with one of her pupils, telling him that he is lazy and disobedient, and that he will never pass his examinations unless he works very much harder. The pupil takes no notice at all.

_____

15   A committee was set up to organise the music concert. They planned it very carefully. As a result the event went very smoothly.

_____

16   Unless we can get at least twenty thousand pounds, our village church will be pulled down. We have written to local companies asking for money, but not one of them has offered anything.

_____

5   Review

What is the expression that corresponds to each of these pictures?

17 _____   18 _____   19 _____

_____   _____   _____

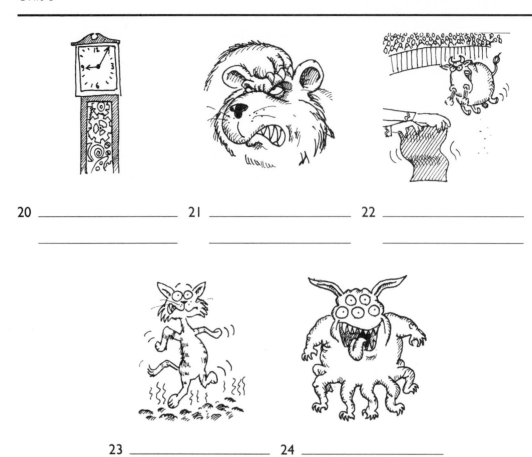

20 _____   21 _____   22 _____

_____   _____   _____

23 _____   24 _____

_____   _____

Now, write sentences using each expression to show that you know their meaning.

25 _____

26 _____

27 _____

28 _____

29 _____

30 _____

31 _____

32 _____

9 Sayings connected with people's attitudes 1

There are sayings and expressions which refer to the way people think or react, eg, someone who is careful with money might say to you *Waste not want not* or *Look after the pennies and the pounds will look after themselves.*

Expressions	Meaning
to dot your i's and cross your t's	to be accurate
to call a spade a spade	to be frank
to make a mountain out of a molehill	to exaggerate
to turn over a new leaf	to reform

1 Make sentences for each pair of pictures using the expressions above.

Why is he making such a fuss?

1 Well, he always _____

_____

What's happened to old Fred?
He used to be so dirty and untidy.

2 Believe it or not, he's _____

_____

Would you say that she was a very tactful person?

3 Not in the least! She always _____

_____

What's the best way to impress the new teacher?

4 Make sure _____

_____

27

2 Replace the underlined words with an expression based on the word given in brackets.

  5 When Management and Trade Unions negotiate over pay and working conditions, it is better if they speak very plainly to each other. (*spade*)

  _____

  6 It is easy to see that John is a lawyer. Even when he is only explaining something simple to his family or writing a personal letter, he likes to make sure that every statement is completely accurate. (*dot*)

  _____

  7 A: Look at this mess! I'm sick and tired of coming home and finding the house turned into a pigsty! Why can't the children put their things away tidily like normal people?
   B: Oh, do be quiet, father! You're really making a lot of fuss about nothing, you know. (*mountain*)

  _____

  8 A: Well, it's about time they stopped misbehaving. (*leaf*)

  _____

3 You might hear people use the following well-known sayings. These sayings are so well known that often the speaker will only say the first part, knowing that the listener will provide the second part.

Every cloud . . .	(has a silver lining.)
If at first you don't succeed, . . .	(try, try, try again.)
It takes all sorts . . .	(to make a world.)
Two heads . . .	(are better than one.)
When in Rome, . . .	(do as the Romans do.)

Complete each sentence with one of the sayings.

  9 A person who does not believe in giving up easily would say

  _____

  10 A person who is an optimist believes that

  _____

  11 A person who likes to consult others before coming to a decision believes that

  _____

12 A person who believes you should try to fit in with your surroundings would say

_____

13 A person who is tolerant of others believes that

_____

4   Use the sayings from Exercise 3 to comment on these situations.

14 Mary and her husband always discuss everything together to make sure that they reach the best decision.

_____

15 When I visit another country, I try to learn a few words of the language, and to adapt to their way of doing things.

_____

16 Things may look bad for you at the moment, but something good usually comes out of even the worst situations.

_____

17 In my village, there are some very strange characters. There's a man who wears women's clothes, a woman who sweeps the road outside her house every morning, a married couple who are always screaming at each other in public.

_____

5   Review

Fill in the missing words in these conversations.

18 A: I'm just in time for my appointment.

B: Come on, let's _____ a spade _____ _____: you're not in time for it, you're 10 minutes too late!

19 A: I'm in trouble at work again.

B: Why? What's happened this time?

A: The usual: arriving late and leaving early.

B: Well, it seems to me that you ought to make a resolution to _____ over a

_____ _____.

20 A: If you're not sure what career to take up, talk things over with your friend Bill.

B: Why should I? What does he know about careers?

A: Not much, perhaps, but two _____ are _____ _____ one.

21 A: I can't solve this problem. I'm hopeless at mathematics!

B: Now, don't give up. Remember: if _____ _____ you don't _____, try, try,

try _____.

22 A: Is the contract ready for signature yet?

B: Almost. It's just a matter now of _____ the i's and _____ the t's.

23 A: Do you think I sometimes overreact?

B: Well, to tell you the truth, you do seem to _____ _____ out of _____
sometimes.

24 A: Four o'clock. Time for a siesta.

B: But I never go to bed in the afternoon.

A: Come on, this is Spain. When in Rome, _____ _____ the Romans _____.

25 A: Nothing seems to be going right for me at the moment.

B: Cheer up! Every _____ has a _____ _____.

26 A: Look at those punks over there. Don't they look stupid with their hair dyed green and
all that metal stuck to their clothes?

B: Don't be so intolerant! It _____ all _____ to _____ _____ _____,
you know.

10 Succeeding and not succeeding

Expressions	
succeeding	not succeeding
to be streets ahead of someone/something	**to fight a losing battle**
performing well	performing badly
to make a good job of something	**to make a mess of something**

I Make sentences for these pictures using the expressions above.

Have you seen Roger's sandcastle?

I Yes, he's certainly _____

2 Oh dear, he's really _____

What's the situation in the race now?

3 Number 6 is _____

4 Number 12 is _____

2   Replace the underlined words with an expression based on the word given in brackets.

   5   Michael's nearly finished building his garage and I must say he's <u>doing it very well</u>. (*job*)

   _____

   6   Poor old Geoffrey – he's <u>trying so hard to get thin</u> and he's fatter than he was before. (*battle*)

   _____

   7   Of course everyone knows that Porsches are <u>much better-designed cars than</u> Fords. (*streets*)

   _____

   8   When you get nervous, you often <u>do things badly</u>. (*mess*)

   _____

3   You might hear the idiomatic expressions which are underlined in these sentences. Which ones are about **performing well/succeeding** (circle A) and which ones are about **performing badly/not succeeding** (circle B)?

9	You'll have to study very hard if you want to <u>make the grade</u> and become a doctor.	A	B
10	I took a job as a teacher, but unfortunately <u>I didn't make a go of it</u>, so I went back to my office job.	A	B
11	All Ray's wonderful plans for his daughter's wedding <u>have fallen flat</u>. She's decided not to get married.	A	B
12	My new motorbike is fantastic! <u>It goes like a bomb!</u>	A	B
13	My daughter doesn't listen to a word I say. Trying to make her pay attention is like <u>banging your head against a brick wall</u>.	A	B
14	Gill's just published her first novel. The critics say <u>it's going to be a roaring success</u>.	A	B

4   Use expressions underlined in Exercise 3 to comment on these situations.

   15   The party was terrible. Only two people came.

   _____

   16   Jack and Anna really tried hard, but their marriage still didn't succeed.

   _____

17 You know you've done well if you're asked to star in a James Bond film.

_____

18 I've asked him to turn his music down hundreds of times but he doesn't take any notice.

_____

19 My new car gets me to work in half the time.

_____

5   Review

Fill in the missing words in this text.

20 My cousin Alfie always wanted to be successful in life. But he hated school and didn't

_____ _____ _____ of it. His friends were always _____ _____

_____ him. He had several jobs and _____ _____ _____ _____ all of

them. All his plans _____ _____. He began to feel he was _____ _____

_____ _____ _____ _____ _____. He started to think he would

never _____ _____ _____ in anything. Until one day last year he was offered

a job in a circus. Now he is _____ _____ _____. He is the best lion tamer

they've ever had!

11 Achieving and not achieving

Expressions	
achievable	not achievable
to get to grips with something	**to get nowhere fast**
achieved	not achieved
to go according to plan	**to be a dead loss**

1 Make sentences for each pair of pictures using the expressions.

Has father put up that tent yet?

1 Well, I think he's _____

_____

2 Not yet. In fact he's _____

_____

How was the wedding?

3 Wonderful! Everything _____

_____

Did you have a good holiday?

4 No, _____

_____

2   Replace the underlined words with an expression based on the word given in brackets.

   5 The May Day parade was very well organised. Everything <u>went perfectly</u>. (*plan*)

   _____

   6 I'm going to bed. All the TV programmes <u>are rubbish</u> tonight. (*loss*)

   _____

   7 I've been trying to learn French for six months now and I <u>can't speak a word of it yet</u>.
   (*nowhere*)

   _____

   8 Ralph's <u>getting better at</u> riding his bicycle at last. (*grips*)

   _____

3   You might hear the idiomatic expressions which are underlined in these sentences.
   Which ones are about **achieving** (circle A) and which ones are about **not achieving** (circle
   B)?

   9 Tom's appearance <u>is going from bad to worse</u>. Now he doesn't wash or shave.   A   B
   10 No one's perfect, but you must always <u>do your best</u>.   A   B
   11 Beating me at chess is <u>a piece of cake</u> for my 8-year-old brother – he's so
   much better than I am.   A   B
   12 He said he could run ten kilometres in ten minutes, but <u>it was easier said than
   done</u>.   A   B
   13 Shy people often <u>don't make it</u> in show business.   A   B
   14 I tell you I'll be rich one day – <u>no problem</u>!   A   B

4   Use the expressions underlined in Exercise 3 to comment on these situations.

   15 Maria always tried hard at school.

   _____

   16 Cutting down that tree was more difficult than it looked.

   _____

   17 Old Ben only had a cold, but then he got pneumonia.

   _____

18 I thought it would be difficult to drive a bus, but in fact it was very easy.

_____

19 It's not difficult to make a promise – it sometimes is to keep it.

_____

20 People who don't try, don't succeed.

_____

5   Review

Fill in the missing words in this text.

21 Johnny wanted to earn a lot of money, and thought that being a rock star must be

_____ _____ _____ _____. So he and three friends formed a band,

learned a few songs and soon made a record which went to Number 2. '_____

_____,' they thought, 'from now on.' They made another record, but unfortunately

this one _____ _____ _____. They made four more which all _____

_____ _____. Things _____ _____ _____ _____ _____. Soon

they had no money and Johnny had to get a job as a cleaner. 'Being a famous rock star,'

said Johnny, 'is _____ _____ _____ _____.'

12 Making comparisons about people's appearance

To make a comparison clearer or more colourful, we use the pattern:

X is as ADJECTIVE as Y.

For example, if someone is very clever and cunning, we might say: *He is as cunning as a fox*.

The following can all be used to describe people's usual physical appearance or condition:

bald **as bald as a coot**		fit **as fit as a fiddle**	
blind **as blind as a bat**		pretty **as pretty as a picture**	
brown **as brown as a berry**		strong **as strong as an ox**	
deaf **as deaf as a post**		thin **as thin as a rake**	

1   Describe this old man:

    1   He cannot see very well.

     _____

    2   He cannot hear very well.

     _____

    3   He has no hair.

     _____

    4   He is very underweight.

     _____

2   Describe this young girl:

    5   She has a good suntan.

     _____

    6   She is very attractive.

     _____

    7   She is very healthy.

     _____

    8   She can lift heavy things easily.

     _____

3   You might hear idiomatic expressions to describe how people can be:

    9 cool (= calm)   **10 proud**   **11 sharp** (= clever, quick-witted)   **12 stubborn.**

Match the adjectives to the pictures.

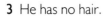

   a   **b**   **c**   **d**

Now complete the sentences using the adjectives.

13 Sometimes she will do anything you ask her to, but on other occasions she can be as

_____ as a mule.

14 You can imagine how he felt when his son won a scholarship to University: he was as

_____ as a peacock.

15 When the car went off the road, everybody screamed and panicked, except for the

Frenchman, who remained as _____ as a cucumber.

16 Mark is an excellent salesman. When it comes to arguing about prices, he's as _____
as a razor.

4   Use the expressions from Exercise 3 to comment on these situations.

17 Jenny believes that her husband is the most handsome man in the world. How does she
feel to be seen in public with him?

_____

18 Most teachers get very angry with pupils who are noisy. How would you describe
teachers who never lose their temper?

_____

19 How would you describe the sort of person who is never fooled by what other people
say to him/her?

_____

20 When Mrs Brown has decided something, nothing you can say will make her change her
mind. How would you describe such a woman?

_____

5   Review

What is the expression that corresponds to each of these pictures?

21 _____

22 _____

23 _____

24 _____

25 _____

26 _____

27 _____

28 _____

29 _____

30 _____

31 _____

32 _____

Now, write sentences using each expression to show their meaning.

33 _____

34 _____

35 _____

36 _____

37 _____

38 _____

39 _____

40 _____

41 _____

42 _____

43 _____

44 _____

13 Sayings connected with people's attitudes 2

Here are some more sayings used to describe the way people react (see Unit 9).

Expressions	Meaning
to live and let live	to be tolerant
it's no use crying over spilt milk	not to regret something that went wrong
to have your cake and eat it	to want more than you can have
to have several irons in the fire	to have many plans and projects at one time

1 Make captions for each picture using one of the expressions.

Don't they get angry with each other?

1 Not at all. They _____

_____

Paul and Brenda lost their car, didn't they?

2 Yes, but _____

_____

Monty wants to get fit, but he doesn't like exercise.

3 He wants _____

_____

Has Phil got any plans to get a job, then?

4 Oh, yes, he's _____

_____

42

2 Explain the sentences with an expression based on the word in brackets.

5 Joe wants to be rich but he doesn't want to work. (*cake*)

_____

6 I don't like my sister's husband and she doesn't like mine, but we don't argue at family parties. (*live*)

_____

7 It's too late now to regret what we did. We must think positively. (*milk*)

_____

8 Elizabeth plans to train as a professional singer, dancer, and actress so she can always get a job. (*irons*)

_____

3 You might hear people use the following sayings. Check their meaning in the reference section if you don't know them.

It's the last straw (that breaks the camel's back).
One man's meat is another man's poison.
It's like the blind leading the blind.
It's the thin end of the wedge.

Complete each sentence with one of the sayings.

9 First he sold our television, then the car, but when he sold the house _____

_____

10 I love the sun and George hates it, but as they say, _____

_____

11 To begin with my brother wanted to stay for a week, but six months later he's still here

and I can see that the first week was only _____

_____

12 Neither the Managing Director nor the Financial Director had any idea how to run the

company; _____

_____

4   **Use the sayings in Exercise 3 to comment on these situations.**

13 My sister prefers living in England to living in America. Personally I much prefer America.

_____

14 There wasn't a problem when my friend moved into my flat, but now all his friends have

moved in too.

_____

15 This last shock was too much for Michael. He's in a mental hospital now and is very ill.

_____

16 Pablo and Ida want to help each other learn English. But the trouble is, neither of them

speaks a word of it.

_____

5   **Review**

Fill in the missing words in these dialogues.

17 A: I'd love to live in the country.

B: Would you? I'd hate it. It's so boring.

A: Yes, but the city's so noisy.

B: Ah well, _____

18 A: I hear you lost your house in that terrible fire.

B: That's right.

A: And you're going to Australia to build another one?

B: Sure! It's _____

19 A: Brian's going to teach Mark to play the guitar.

B: But Brian can't play the guitar!

A: I know. It's going to be _____

20 A: You've got a good job, a nice house, the children, me ... what more do you want?

B: Six months holiday a year.

A: The trouble with you is you want _____

14 Knowing and not knowing

Expressions	
knowing	not knowing
to know all about	not to know the first thing about
to know a thing or two about	not to be able to tell one end of
	something from the other
to know a place like the back of your hand	not to have the foggiest idea

I Make sentences for each pair of pictures using the expressions.

Is your brother an expert on old sports cars?

I Yes, he _____   **2** No, he _____

_____   _____

What about you?

3 Well, yes, I _____   **4** Me? I can't _____

_____   _____

Do you know where we are?

5 Yes. I know this place _____   **6** No. I haven't _____

_____   _____

2   Replace the underlined words with an expression based on the word(s) given in brackets. Make any changes that are necessary.

   7 He may look stupid, but he <u>has a lot of experience of</u> life. (*two*)

   _____

   8 I used to <u>be very familiar with</u> Madrid, but it's years since I was last there. (*hand*)

   _____

   9 I <u>cannot explain</u> why there is no butter in the refrigerator. (*foggiest*)

   _____

   10 <u>It's no good asking me about electronic keyboards.</u> (*one end*)

   _____

   11 If you want to know anything about pop music, ask Melanie: <u>she's the expert.</u> (*all*)

   _____

   12 They asked me to write a book on astrophysics. The trouble is, <u>it's not a subject that I have ever studied.</u> (*first thing*)

   _____

3   You might hear the idiomatic expressions which are underlined in these sentences. Which ones are about **knowing** (circle A) and which are about **not knowing** (circle B)?

   13 'Is that the sun or the moon up there?'
         'I <u>haven't a clue</u>! I'm a stranger here too!'   A   B
   14 The receptionist at this hotel is very helpful: she has all the information <u>at her fingertips.</u>   A   B
   15 'Who's the present Director of Studies at the College?'
         'I don't know, I'm <u>a bit out of touch</u>, I'm afraid.'   A   B
   16 If there's anything you're not sure about, ask old George: he knows the job <u>inside out.</u>   A   B
   17 Many companies put a new employee next to an older one, who really <u>knows the ropes.</u>   A   B

4   Use the expressions underlined in Exercise 3 to comment on these situations.

   18 I've been away, so I really don't know what's going on.

   _____

19 We have an excellent teacher, who knows her subject very well indeed.

_____

20 Somebody asks you a question, and you want to make it very clear that you do **not know** the answer.

_____

21 The boss's secretary has been with the company for seventeen years.

_____

5   Review

Fill in the missing words in these texts.

22 A: How well do you know London?

B: Like the _____ of my _____!

A: Good. So, please tell me where Buckingham Palace is.

B: I _____ _____ _____ idea.

A: I thought you said you knew this city _____ _____?

B: I do, but I haven't got a _____ where Buckingham Palace is.

A: Why not?

B: I'm a Republican.

23 John is crazy about his new personal computer. He has stored lots of things on **it, because,** as he says, he likes to _____ the information _____ his fingertips. When **he first** got it, he didn't know the _____ thing _____ computers (I'm the same: **I can't tell** one _____ of a computer _____ the _____). But he soon learned _____ about them, and now, every day, he sits at his PC hoping that someone will ask **him a** question!

15 Conforming and not conforming

Expressions	
conforming	not conforming
to pay lip service to something	**to do your own thing**
to toe the line	**to go your own way**

1 Make sentences for each pair of pictures using the expressions.

Joe looks different from the rest of them, doesn't he?

1 I know. He never wants to _____

_____

2 Yes. He always wants _____

_____

Sergeant Green says he agrees with the drinking and driving laws.

3 No, he only _____

_____

So Maribelle doesn't want to come with us?

4 No, she prefers to _____

_____

2   Replace the underlined words with an expression based on the word given in brackets.

   5 He always does exactly what he wants. (*thing*)

   _____

   6 When you join the army you have to do the same as everybody else. (*line*)

   _____

   7 I was a secretary for the Nationalist Party, but I only pretended to agree with their policies. (*lip*)

   _____

   8 You always do exactly the opposite of what people tell you to do. (*way*)

   _____

3   You might hear the idiomatic expressions which are underlined in these sentences. Which ones are about **conforming/joining in** (circle A) and which ones are about **not conforming/not joining in** (circle B)?

9 When Les's neighbour bought a new Volvo, Les had to buy one too. He always has to keep up with the Joneses.	A	B
10 John took the law into his own hands when he hit the burglar.	A	B
11 Henry's not very adventurous when he cooks. He always goes by the book.	A	B
12 David's painted his house a horrible yellow colour. Now it stands out like a sore thumb from the rest of the street.	A	B
13 Geraldine is the perfect driver. She always obeys the letter of the law.	A	B
14 Ramon hates living in England. He's like a fish out of water in a cold wet climate.	A	B

4   Use the expressions underlined in Exercise 3 to comment on these situations.

   15 Rudolf's bright pink hair certainly makes him look different – and terrible!

   _____

   16 I think Mandy's bought a new microwave just because Gill's got one.

   _____

   17 Michael always reads all the instructions before he does anything.

   _____

18 Poor little Denis. He doesn't fit in with the other children and hates playing with them.

_____

19 You should never try to approach a dangerous criminal.

_____

20 Old Fred is the perfect citizen. For example, he never never drives over the speed limit!

_____

5   Review

Fill in the missing words in this text.

21 Albert was a very independent young man who always liked to _____ _____

_____ _____. When he was in the army he hated having to _____ _____

_____. He felt like _____ _____ _____ _____ _____. He refused

to _____ _____ _____ _____ and was always being punished for doing

things his own way. The army doesn't like individuals who behave differently from the

group and _____ _____ _____ _____ _____ _____, and in the

end they discharged him. Now he's _____ _____ _____ _____. I hear he's

travelling around Europe as a pavement artist.

16 Making comparisons about actions

To emphasise an action, we often use the pattern *do X like Y*, ie we do X in the way that Y would do it. For example, if someone eats a lot, you could say: *He eats like a horse.*

Expressions	Meaning
to drink like a fish	to drink a lot of alcohol
to smoke like a chimney	to smoke heavily
to spend money like water	to spend freely
to hang on like grim death	not to let go

1 Make captions for each picture using the expressions.

Sue's always buying new clothes.

1 Yes, she _____

_____

Did you know Uncle Bernard fell over a cliff?

2 Yes, but they say he _____

_____

Marjorie buys 60 cigarettes a day.

3 I know. She _____

_____

Your brother seems to enjoy his beer!

4 Yes, I'm afraid he _____

_____

2   Use expressions from the list above to replace the words underlined in these sentences.

5 Most of us would love a chance to go shopping and <u>buy everything we want</u>.

_____

6 Ronald will kill himself with <u>all those cigars</u>.

_____

7 Vince had <u>much too much beer</u> at the party.

_____

8 Someone tried to steal my mother's handbag, but she <u>held onto it</u> and in the end the thief ran away.

_____

3   You might hear idiomatic expressions which emphasise that you **cannot**, **did not** or **will not** do something. Complete the expressions below with a word from the list.

a/another	drop	a	wink
	step		bite
	thing		note

9 He didn't drink _____

10 We didn't eat _____

11 I mustn't say _____

12 She can't sing _____

13 They won't sleep _____

14 I can't walk _____

4   Use the expressions in Exercise 3 to react to these situations.

15 Would you like some cake?

_____

16 Oh, please tell me the secret!

_____

17 Don't you want to come down to the river with me?

_____

18 Would you like to join our pop group?

_____

19 Have another cup of tea, Mr Smith.

_____

20 Why are you looking so tired?

_____

5   Review

What is the expression that corresponds to each of these pictures?

21 _____   22 _____   23 _____

_____   _____   _____

24 _____   25 _____   26 _____

_____   _____   _____

27 _____   28 _____   29 _____

_____   _____   _____

Now, write sentences using each expression to show its meaning.

30 _____

31 _____

32 _____

33 _____

34 _____

35 _____

36 _____

37 _____

38 _____

17 Sayings connected with people's attitudes 3

Here are some more sayings and expressions which refer to the way people think or react.

Expressions	Meaning
to kill two birds with one stone	to perform one action with the result that another action is achieved as well
it's better late than never	it's better to do something late than never at all
to put the cart before the horse	to do things in an illogical order
great minds think alike	two people think of the same thing at the same moment

1 Make sentences for each picture using one of the expressions.

I thought John went to Florida on business?

1 Yes! But he decided to _____

_____

Larry always does his Christmas shopping at the last minute, doesn't he?

2 Well, I suppose it's _____

_____

Sue's bought a new car and she hasn't passed her driving test yet.

3 Yes, I think she's _____

_____

Mr and Mrs Boswell often have the same ideas.

4 Yes, _____

_____

2 Replace the underlined words with an expression based on the word given in brackets.

5 My grandfather didn't go abroad until he was 86. He said it <u>was always something he'd wanted to do.</u> (*late*)

_____

6 Trevor tried to <u>use one big pot to cook the chicken and the fish at the same time.</u> (*birds*)

_____

7 My sister and I often buy the same clothes without realising. We say it's because <u>clever people often have the same ideas.</u> (*great*)

_____

8 Buying the furniture before you've got the house is <u>doing things in the wrong order.</u> (*cart*)

_____

3 You might hear people use the following sayings:

Expressions	Meaning
to bite off more than you can chew	to take on more than you are able to do
to lock the stable door after the horse has gone/bolted	to make security arrangements after a break-in, etc.
out of sight, out of mind	if you can't see something you don't think about it
to practise what you preach	to do what you tell other people to do

Complete each sentence with one of the sayings.

9 I don't think of Joe when I don't see him. It's _____

_____

10 To put locks on the doors after a burglary is to _____

_____

11 If you agree to do more than you have time for, you are _____

_____

12 Julius always tells others what they should do, but never follows his own advice. People like him should _____

4   Use the expressions from Exercise 3 to react to these situations.

13 Fred only started locking his car after his cassette player was stolen.

_____

14 Miriam got very tired when she started doing an evening job as well as her daytime one.

_____

15 My teacher is always late, but tells us we must be on time.

_____

16 Norman doesn't like his job at all, but he never thinks about it at weekends.

_____

5   Review

Fill in the missing words in these dialogues.

17 A: I'm thinking of writing a book.

B: And when are you going to do that? You work all week.

A: Well, there's evenings, weekends, holidays . . .

B: It sounds easy, but make sure you don't _____

18 A: I've just had a great idea.

B: Oh?

A: I'm going to learn to water ski.

B: That's amazing – I thought the same thing yesterday!

A: Ah, you see _____

19 A: Don't come in here with your dirty shoes on.

B: Oh, sorry . . . but look, you've got paint all over your coat!

A: Where? Oh yes, so I have!

B: You ought to _____

20 A: I'm going to buy a video recorder.

B: But you haven't got a TV, have you?

A: No, but . . .

B: Don't you think that's _____

21 A: I hate my maths teacher.

B: Do you?

A: And I hate my French teacher, and I hate my history teacher, and I . . .

B: Oh, come on, Steve, we're on holiday! Forget it. You know _____

_____

18 Conversational phrases 1

In conversations, we try to persuade each other, make suggestions, agree, disagree, confirm, deny, and so on. To make our points more strongly, we use expressions. For example, instead of just replying *No* to a question beginning with *Do you mind ...?*, we might say *Not at all!* or *Not in the least.*: *Do you mind if I ask you something? Not at all.*

Here are some examples to show how they fit into a sentence. Look in the reference section to check their meaning, if you are unsure.

Expressions	Examples
Let's face it,	Let's face it, nobody's perfect. (we both know this)
What about ...?	What about having a party this weekend?
or something.	Have a cake or a bun or a biscuit or something.
It's all very well, but	It's all very well staying up late every night, but I have to get up early in the morning.
the fact of the matter is	the fact of the matter is I still love him, although he doesn't love me.
at that	She was an intelligent girl, and a pretty one at that.
put it this way	He wasn't very rational ... put it this way, he was mad.
after all,	After all, I've always admitted that I'm lazy.
for a start	Well, you had three sandwiches, two bananas and a hamburger for a start, and that was before dinner.
if you ask me	If you ask me, old Mrs Blott never knew the people in the flat upstairs were escaped convicts.
nothing of the sort!	'You took that girl's handbag, didn't you?' 'I did nothing of the sort!'
it's just that	I wanted to come to your party, it's just that my mother was ill and I had to stay and look after her.

1 Study these two conversations. First, the basic conversation, without any conversational expressions. Then, the same conversation, but with conversational expressions added.

[Bob is a draughtsman. He has been out of work for the last eighteen months. His girlfriend, Val, is trying to persuade him to train for a different job].

Basic conversation

Val: Bob, you'll never get any work as a draughtsman in this town. Go on one of these government re-training schemes. Learn to be an electrician.

Bob: Training schemes are all right, but I'm a good draughtsman. Why should I train to be an electrician?

Val: Why shouldn't you? Lots of people train for other jobs nowadays.

Bob: I'll tell you why not. I'm too old.

Val: Rubbish! People in their fifties go on training schemes. You're just looking for excuses. You just don't like change.

Bob: That's not true! But I don't see why I should have to change my trade.

Conversation with expressions

Val: <u>Let's face it</u>, Bob, you'll never get any work as a draughtsman in this town. So, <u>what about</u> going on one of these government re-training schemes? Learn to be an electrician <u>or something</u>.

Bob: Training schemes are <u>all very well</u>, but <u>the fact of the matter is</u>, I'm a draughtsman, and a good one <u>at that</u>. Why should I train to be an electrician?

Val: <u>Put it this way</u>: why shouldn't you? <u>After all</u>, lots of people train for other jobs nowadays.

Bob: I'll tell you why not. <u>For a start</u>, I'm too old.

Val: Rubbish! People in their fifties go on training schemes. <u>If you ask me</u>, you're just looking for excuses. <u>Let's face it</u>, you just don't like change.

Bob: <u>Nothing of the sort!</u> <u>It's just that</u> I don't see why I should have to change my trade.

2   Here is a similar conversation. Add conversational expressions based on the word given in brackets.

Bob: I wish I could get a job!

Val: 1 (*face*) _____ Bob, there aren't any jobs for draughtsmen around here.

    2 (*ask*)_____, you ought to go on a government re-training scheme? 3 (*about*)

    _____ learning to be an electrician 4 (*something*) _____?

Bob: Well, 5 (*start*) _____ I'm not interested in electrical work.

Val: That's 6 (*well*) _____, but 7 (*matter*) _____ that you've been out of work

    for a year and a half and you've got to do something about it. 8 (*way*) _____: it's

    better to do a job you don't like than to have no job at all.

Bob: 9 (*face*) _____, Val, I'm never going to get work in this town. Anyway, I'm too old

    to start re-training.

Val: You're 10 (*nothing*) _____. What's the real reason you don't want to go on a

    training course? Are you afraid?

Bob: No. 11 (*just*) _____ I don't see why I should have to change my trade. 12 (*all*)

    _____, I'm a qualified draughtsman, and a good one 13 (*that*) _____.

3   Match these cartoons with their captions.

A   B

C   D

14 'Let's face it, darling, you are no Olympic champion!'

15 'Put it this way, he's not marrying her just for love.'

16 'If you ask me, she's giving it too much water!'

17 The fact of the matter is, I never really wanted to be a doctor in the first place.

4   Review

Use the conversational expressions in sentences of your own to complete these dialogues. We have done the first one to help you.

18 **What about . . .?**

A: I'd like to do something exciting this weekend.

B: _What about going to the seaside ?_

19 **or something**

A: I'm hungry!

B: _____

20 all very well

A: You ought to try to lose weight!

B: _____

21 at that

A: Tell me about the new Principal of your school.

B: _____

22 After all ...

A: Why do you keep talking about my family?

B: _____

23 For a start

A: Why don't you come to the football match with us?

B: _____

24 nothing of the sort!

A: You told Jenny that I was going out with another girl, didn't you?

B: _____

25 It's just that

A: Why have you stopped going out with Michael?

B: _____

19 Conversational phrases 2

Here are some more examples of everyday phrases used in conversation. Look in the reference section to check their meaning if you are unsure.

Expressions	Examples
There's no way	There's no way I'd trust my sister's opinion about clothes.
in other words	I respect him, I admire him . . . in other words I think a lot of him.
in a nutshell	I think she's aggressive, bad mannered . . . rude, in a nutshell.
Talk about	Talk about rich! He paid for our dinner which cost more than a week's wages for me!
anyway . . .	He's completely mad but I love him anyway.
once and for all	I'm telling you once and for all NOT to take my records without asking.
. . ., and that's that.	I don't believe your story and that's that.
I like that!	'The boss told me you didn't have much work.' 'Well I like that! I'm doing three people's jobs at the moment!'
That'll be the day!	'They say we're getting a 10% bonus this year.' 'Huh! That'll be the day! We've never had a bonus yet.'
Come on . . .	Come on, tell me where you've put my calculator!
better still . . .	You could stay with me for the weekend – better still, you could come for the whole week.
No way!	No way would I give him a penny!

1 Study these two conversations. First, the basic conversation, without any conversational expressions. Then, the same conversation, but with conversational expressions added. Try to guess what they mean.

[*Val is trying to persuade Bob to take a training course. Bob says that he doesn't see why he should change from being an actor, even if he is out of work*]

Basic conversation

Bob: I won't change my profession.
Val: So you'd rather be an out-of-work actor than a well-paid electrician. That's it, isn't it?
Bob: Val, when you decide something, you never listen to anyone, do you? You are stubborn! I am NOT going on any training scheme.
Val: ME stubborn? YOU are the one that's really pig-headed. And this is all the thanks I get for trying to be helpful. Well, if that's the way you feel, I won't say another word.
Bob: I don't believe you! Let's change the subject. Come here and sit next to me.
Val: No! I only sit next to well-paid electricians!

Conversation with expressions

Bob: There's no way I'm going to change my profession.

Val: In other words, you'd rather be an out-of-work actor than a well-paid electrician. That's it in a nutshell, isn't it?

Bob: I know you, Val. When you decide something, you never listen to anyone, do you? Talk about stubborn! Anyway, once and for all, I am NOT going on any training scheme, and that's that.

Val: ME stubborn? I like that! YOU are the one that's really pig-headed. And this is all the thanks I get for trying to be helpful. Well, if that's the way you feel, I won't say another word.

Bob: That'll be the day! Come on, let's change the subject. Better still, come here and sit next to me.

Val: No way! I only sit next to well-paid electricians!

2 Here is a similar conversation. Add conversational expressions based on the word(s) given in brackets.

Bob: 1 (*once*) _____, Val, I don't want to go on a training scheme. And 2 (*any*) _____ I'm too old to learn new skills.

Val: Really, Bob, you can be difficult when you want to.

Bob: Me? Difficult? 3 (*like*) _____! You're the one who keeps going on about training, not me. Why don't you shut up about training? Or, 4 (*better*) _____, why don't YOU go on a training scheme?

Val: 5 (*way*) _____! I'm not the one who's out of work!

Bob: 6 (*words*) _____, you wouldn't want to change your job, either. That's it, 7 (*nutshell*) _____, isn't it?

Val: 8 (*talk*) _____ argumentative! 9 (*on*) _____, Bob, you can't just sit there for the rest of your life. Give them a ring.

Bob: Look, 10 (*no*) _____ I'm going to go on a training scheme, 11 (*that*) _____. I'll soon get a great acting job.

Val: 12 (*day*) _____!

3 Match these cartoons with their captions.

A

B

C

D

13 'Talk about quick-tempered! You should see him when he's really angry!' ☐

14 'Once and for all, I'm not taking you out again today, and that's that.' ☐

15 'That'll be the day!' ☐

16 'Talk about crowded! I think the whole population of Spain is here.' ☐

4 Review

Use the conversational expressions in sentences of your own to complete these dialogues.

17 **and that's that!**

A: I want a hi-fi and a video recorder for my birthday, daddy.

B: _____

18 **I like that!**

A: You oughtn't to smoke so much.

B: _____

19 Talk about ...!

A: Can I have another cake? I'm still hungry.

B: _____

20 In other words

A: I know I said we would go to the disco tonight, but I don't really feel like going out.

B: _____

21 There's no way ...

A: (*Wife to husband*): Would you like to give my mother a ring?

B: _____

22 in a nutshell

A: What was it like in the army, grandad?

B: _____

23 better still ...

A: (*One woman to another*): I'd love to live in a bigger flat with a balcony, wouldn't you?

B: _____

20 Conversational phrases 3

Look at this further set of phrases used in conversation with some example sentences. Use the Reference section to check any meanings you don't understand.

Expressions	Examples
and so on	You'll need onions, tomatoes, peppers, mushrooms and so on.
as well	I don't only like rock music, I like classical as well.
change the subject	Whenever I want to talk to you about your homework, you always change the subject.
as well as	I like classical music as well as rock.
to say nothing of	That cat ate all the fish, to say nothing of the turkey!
not to mention	That cat ate all the fish, not to mention the turkey.
It's a good job	It's a good job your father wasn't alone when he fell ill.
Not a chance!	'Do you want me to drive you to the airport.' 'Not a chance! You haven't passed your test!'
let alone	I haven't had time for a cup of tea yet, let alone a sit down.
By the way ...	By the way, did you know that Franny got married?
or so	For a week you'll need jeans, smart trousers and about six shirts or so.
some ... or other	We'll get a room in some hotel or other.
(not) ... at all	I don't like him at all.
It stands to reason	It stands to reason you're tired – you've been working for sixteen hours.
When it comes to X, ...	When it comes to glamour, Ada Baggs certainly hasn't got it.
a wet blanket	It's no use taking John to parties – he's a real wet blanket and always wants to go home at ten o'clock.

1 Study this conversation looking at the conversational expressions underlined.

[Brian is thinking of going to Africa on safari. His friend Ralph is discussing the idea with him.]

Ralph: You'll need tropical clothing. You know, cotton shirts, lightweight trousers, and so on. You'll need to take some medications with you as well.

Brian: Just think of the game parks! All those wonderful wild animals!

Ralph: Don't change the subject! Be practical. Have you thought about the health problems? There's typhoid and cholera to consider, as well as malaria, to say nothing of dysentery and hepatitis.

Brian: Not to mention Aids and leprosy! Don't be such a pessimist, Ralph! Just think of all the good things: driving across the bush in a Land Rover, camping out under the stars ...

Ralph: It's a good job I don't take you seriously, Brian!

Brian: But I AM serious! Look, why don't you come with me? You'd love it, I'm sure. We could even hire a canoe and go down the Zambesi.

Ralph: Not a chance, Brian! I would get seasick crossing the river here on the ferryboat, let alone in a canoe down the Zambesi. By the way, how long do you intend to go for?

Brian: Oh, about two years or so.

Ralph: Two years? Would your employers give you such a long leave of absence?

Brian: Oh, I'll make up some excuse or other. Anyway, why should I bother to tell them anything at all?

Ralph: Well, it stands to reason that you can't go off on safari for two years without somebody noticing that you are not at your desk.

Brian: Ralph, when it comes to being adventurous, you're a real wet blanket!

2   Here is a similar conversation. Add conversational expressions based on the word(s) given in brackets.

Ralph: You'll need to take a lot of medicines with you: anti-malaria tablets **1** (*on*) _____.

You'll need suntan lotion **2** (*well*) _____.

Brian: **3** (*say nothing*) _____ aspirins and foot powder! Don't be such **4** (*wet*) _____, Ralph!

Ralph: You can laugh, but Africa is a dangerous place, what with tropical diseases and insects, **5** (*mention*) _____ snakes and other wild animals. **6** (*way*) _____, how do you intend to travel?

Brian: By camel. Seriously, Ralph, **7** (*job*) _____ I don't listen to you or I would never go anywhere **8** (*all*) _____. Tell me, how's your wife? Still working at the bank?

Ralph: **9** (*subject*) _____. We're talking about your crazy idea to go on safari. Why don't you give it up? You know it's crazy, **10** (*well*) _____ being dangerous.

Brian: **11** (*chance*) _____! I've been planning the trip for the last year **12** (*so*) _____, and I don't intend to give it up now just because I might get bitten by some insect **13** (*other*) _____. You know me, Ralph. **14** (*comes*) _____ adventure holidays, nothing will stop me. A hungry lion wouldn't put me off, **15** (*alone*) _____ some miserable little insect.

Ralph: All the same, **16** (*reason*) _____ that you cannot go to Africa without at least

thinking about the dangers.

Brian: The only danger is that you might talk me out of it! Let's **17** (*subject*) _____.

How's your wife? Still working at the bank?

3   Match these cartoons with their captions.

18 'When it comes to heavy work, it stands to reason that men are better than women.'

19 'Not a chance! My mother told me never to talk to strange men!'

20 'It has taken me three years or so just to get the hands right, to say nothing of the smile.'

21 'Don't change the subject! Where have you hidden the telephone?'

4 **Review**

Use the conversational expressions in sentences of your own to complete these
dialogues. The prompts in B will help you.

22 and so on

A: What did you two talk about?

B: /just/work/family/children/ _____

23 as well

A: What shall I bring to the barbecue?

B: /steaks/sausages/a bottle of wine/ _____

24 as well as

A: Is it likely to be cold in London?

B: Yes./overcoat/a couple of pullovers/ _____

25 not to mention

A: Was your holiday really bad?

B: /weather/terrible hotel/delays at the airport/ _____

26 It's a good job

A: I'm afraid I've eaten your share of the cake.

B: /not hungry/ _____

27 let alone ...

A: Would you like to come for a walk up Tor Hill with us?

B: /not stand up/climb a hill/ _____

28 By the way ...

A: What do you think of my new dress?

B: It suits you./old dress?/ _____

29 or so

A: How long will it take you to finish your homework?

B: /finish/hour/ _____

30 some ... or other

A: [*conversation between two librarians*] What did that old gentleman want?

B: /old book/ _____

31 (not) ... at all

A: Have you ever been to Italy?

B: /abroad/ _____

Reference section

Abbreviations:

AmE	American English	neg	negative	sg	something
cf	compare	opp	opposite	sim	a similar expression
eg	for example	re	about, concerning	US	American usage
ie	that is	sb	somebody	usu	usually
lit	literally				

Unit

after all, . . . In spite of what has just been said, . . . 18

air, it's all very much (up) in the air: sg is not yet decided: *We were planning to build a house, but it's very much up in the air at the moment.* 6

all, it's all very well, . . .: it might seem to be a good idea but . . . 18

and so on: etcetera. 20

and that's that: emphasising that this is your final word/decision on the subject 19

anyway, . . .: despite/regardless of what has been said before. 19

as well: also. 20

as well as: in addition to. 20

(not) . . . at all: emphasising the negative 20

at that: emphasising the truth of a fact 18

bad, go from bad to worse: start badly and get worse: *We keep running into more and more problems with the new factory. Everything is going from bad to worse.* Sim, **go downhill.** 11

bald, as bald as a coot: the coot is a water bird which has a bald spot on the front of its head. 12

battle, fight a losing battle: make an effort but have no chance of success: *It's no good trying to make Susan give up smoking. You're fighting a losing battle.* 10

bear, like a bear with a sore head: having a headache (a sore head) will make you feel miserable. 8

best, do your best: make the best effort possible. *Sid did his best to understand his daughter but she never accepted him.* Sim, **do your utmost.** 11

bet, I wouldn't bet on it: lit, I would not put money on it to win, ie, I wouldn't depend on it, it is uncertain. 6

bet, You bet!: you can be sure. cf, **I bet!**, often used sarcastically to mean the opposite, ie, I don't believe it. 6

Unit

better late than never: it is better to do something later than you should have done it, than not to do it at all . . . 17

better still, . . .: making a better suggestion than the first one. 19

bite off more than you can chew: try to do more than is possible for you 17

black, **pitch black:** as black as pitch. Usually to describe darkness in the sense of absence of light. 4

blind, **as blind as a bat:** bats are nocturnal animals which find their way by radar rather than by sight. 12

blind, **the blind leading the blind:** describes the situation where the person in charge knows no more than the rest of the people in the group. 13

blue, **sky blue:** as blue as the sky. 4

bomb, **go like a bomb:** go fast, usually of machines, especially cars: *Her new car is wonderful: it goes like a bomb.* 10

book, **an open book:** nothing is hidden 5

book, **go by the book:** do things according to the rules. 15

books, **in sb's good/bad books:** when sb thinks well/badly of you, you are in that person's good/bad books. Often a temporary state. 7

brown, **as brown as a berry:** berries go red or brown in autumn. 12

bull, **a red rag to a bull:** bulls are supposed to get angry at the sight of anything red. 8

By the way, . . .: used when a thought occurs to you, related to what sb else has just said. 20

cake, **a piece of cake:** describes sg which is easy to do: *Can you mend the video, Janet? It's a piece of cake!* cf, **No problem!** 11

cake, **have your cake and eat it:** try to do two things which cannot both be done. Sim, **have it both ways.** *Maria wants to stay slim, but she also*

73

Unit

loves chocolate. Tell her she can't have her cake and eat it: either she gives up chocolate, or she gets fat. 13

cards, be on the cards: be very probable. cards = cards for fortune telling, which try to predict the future 6

cards, play your cards close to your chest: ie, in a card game, hold your cards up so that your opponent cannot see them. 5

cat, let the cat out of the bag: reveal a secret, usually without intending to. 5

cat, like a cat on hot bricks: somebody who is so nervous they can't stay still. AmE **Cat on a hot tin roof** was the title of a play by Tennessee Williams. 8

chance, he didn't have a cat in Hell's chance: a cat would burn to nothing in Hell, therefore, he had no chance at all. 6

change the subject: talk about something else. 20

cheap, dirt cheap: very cheap indeed. 4

clear, crystal clear: Usually re an explanation: *Now that you have explained the situation to me, everything is crystal clear.* 4

clockwork, go like clockwork: to go perfectly, like a piece of machinery. 8

cloud, Every cloud has a silver lining: You know that the sun is shining behind a dark cloud because the sun's rays make the edges of the cloud look bright (*silver*). The word *lining* usually refers to the inner material of a jacket. So, every piece of misfortune hides something much better. 9

clue, not have a clue: not have any idea at all about sg. 14

cold, ice cold: as cold as ice eg, an ice cold beer. 4

Come on, . . .: expressing encouragement. 19

cool, as cool as a cucumber: a cucumber is a watery salad vegetable popular in sandwiches and salads during the hot summer months. *cool* here refers to sb's self control, ie calm. 12

cross, cross the t's. See under **dot.** 9

crush, have a crush on sb: be attracted to sb: *I think he has a crush on me.* Sim, **fancy sb.** 1

Unit

deaf, as deaf as a post: a post, like any other piece of wood, or indeed any other inanimate object, cannot hear. 12

deaf, stone deaf: ie, as deaf as a stone = completely deaf. 4

dot, dot the i's and cross the t's: When children learn handwriting, they are taught that it is quicker to write the whole word out first and then go back and put dots on the i's and crosses on the t's. They must do this carefully. 9

doubt, doubt if there's anything in it: doubt if there is any truth in it. 2

drink, drink like a fish: drink, usually alcohol, in large quantities. 16

drink, not drink a drop: not drink even the smallest quantity of liquid (ie, a drop). 16

drive, drive you up the wall: Sim, **drive you mad:** *Her singing is driving me up the wall/mad.* 1

duck, like water off a duck's back: a duck's feathers are waterproof, so that water runs off easily instead of making a bird's body wet. 8

ears, not believe your ears/eyes: usu with can't/ couldn't: *Marie told me she was pregnant again. I couldn't believe my ears!* 2

earth, like nothing on earth: The expression usually means *bad*, and can be used with other verbs of the senses: *It smells/tastes/sounds like nothing on earth.* 8

easy, easier said than done: describes sg which is more difficult to do than it seems: *They asked me to take a thorn out of the lion's paw, but it was easier said than done.* 11

eat, not eat a bite: not eat anything, ie, not to take even one bite out of sg. 16

end, not to be able to tell one end of something from the other: to say you don't understand, usu re machinery. 14

eyelid, not bat an eyelid: Sim: **not turn a hair:** *She didn't turn a hair/bat an eyelid when the judge sentenced her to 12 years' imprisonment.* 2

fact, the fact of the matter is: emphasising the real truth of the situation. 18

fancy, take a fancy to: be attracted to sb/sg. 1

fingertips, at your fingertips: easily available, handy: *He has all the facts at his fingertips.* 14

Unit

fire, **have several irons in the fire:** have many interests in different, usually business, areas. Sim, **have your finger in several pies.**   13

fish, **like a fish out of water:** be out of place and uncomfortable because you are in the wrong surroundings.   15

fit, **as fit as a fiddle:** a fiddle (popular word for a violin) is 'fit' when it is properly tuned.   12

flat, **fall flat:** describes sg which does not go as well as expected: *The garden party fell flat because of the bad weather.*   10

foot, **put your foot in it:** make an embarrassing mistake: *I really put my foot in it when I told her I didn't like Welsh people. It turned out she was a Welsh Nationalist!*   7

for a start: pointing out a problem or objection. The expression **for a start** (Also, **for one thing . . .**) suggests that this is only the first of several objections you have to make.   18

game, **give the game away:** give away, ie, reveal sg without intending to, as you might accidentally let your opponent see your cards in a game of cards. Sim, **give the show away.**   5

go, **have a go at sb:** attack sb with words, or even physically.   7

go, **make a go of sg:** succeed despite problems and difficulties.   10

grade, **make the grade:** succeed, reach the target.   10

great minds think alike: You usually say this when someone makes a suggestion that you were about to make, ie, you and the other person must be clever to have had the same idea.   17

green, **pea green:** describing a shade of green, ie, the colour of peas.   4

green, **sea green:** describing a shade of green, ie, the colour of the sea.   4

grips, **get to grips with sg:** learn to do sg involving a lot of effort: *She is finally getting to grips with her new computer.*   11

hand, **know a place like the back of your hand:** know a place very well.   14

handle, **fly off the handle.** Sim, **go off the deep end** = lose your temper, become very, very angry.   2

Unit

hang on, **hang on like grim death:** not let go of sg no matter how hard it is to hold on.   16

hard, **rock hard:** very very hard, as hard as a rock: *His muscles are rock hard.*   4

hat, **keep it under your hat:** keep sg a secret. Hat = a place where you can hide money, etc.   5

head over heels in love with sb: very much in love with sb.   1

head, **bang your head against a brick wall:** try again and again but without success: *I've given up trying to persuade Joe to get a proper job: it's like banging your head against a brick wall.*   10

heads, **two heads are better than one:** it's easier for two people to decide sg, than one on his/her own.   9

horse, **a dark horse:** a racing term for an unknown horse which surprises everyone by running well.   5

hot, **piping hot:** Sim, **steaming hot.**   4

hungry, **starving hungry:** so hungry that you are starving.   4

I like that!: expressing disbelief at someone's impudence, unfairness, unreasonableness, etc.   19

idea, **not have the foggiest idea.** Sim, **the slightest/faintest/least idea:** *'What's the capital of Albania?' 'I haven't the slightest idea.'*   14

idle, **bone idle:** idle or lazy right through to the bone.   4

If at first you don't succeed, try, try, try again: Don't give up: keep trying.   9

if you ask me: if you want my opinion, . . .   18

in a nutshell: summarising.   19

in other words: rephrasing someone else's words to make their meaning quite plain and clear.   19

inside out, **to know something inside out:** to know it completely, thoroughly.   14

it's a good job: it is fortunate.   20

it's just that, . . .: the simple truth is . . .   18

it stands to reason: it is clear, logical.   20

it takes all sorts to make a world: There are many different kinds of people, and we should be tolerant rather than expecting everyone else to be like us.   9

Unit

job, make a good/bad job of sg: do sg well/ badly.   10

Joneses, keep up with the Joneses: try to have everything that other people have. The Joneses represent a family that you envy because they have a lot of possessions you would like.   15

jump in with both feet: act without thinking about the consequences: *Tom didn't know anything about his new job when he accepted it. He just jumped in with both feet.* Opp, **look before you leap.**   3

keep sg to yourself: not share your secrets or knowledge with other people.   5

kill two birds with one stone: achieve two different things with one action. Because you have to pass the dry cleaner's on the way to the bank, you can get some money from the bank, and pick up your dry cleaning on the way home.   17

know a thing or two about: know a lot. Sim, **tell sb a thing or two:** *Old Charlie Bester knows a thing or two about what really goes on in this village!*   14

know all about: Sim, **a know-all** for a person who knows or thinks s/he knows a lot.   14

know sg inside out: Sim, **know sg backwards:** *When it comes to local history, old Charlie Bester knows the subject inside out/backwards.*   14

know, not know the first thing about: usually about a subject or a piece of equipment or machinery. In order of emphasis: *I don't know anything about . . . (I don't know a thing about . . .) I don't know the first thing about . . .*   14

lamb, like a lamb to the slaughter: used to emphasise sb's unwillingness to go somewhere. slaughter = the killing of animals for food or in religious ceremonies.   8

law, obey the letter of the law: do exactly what the law requires.   15

law, take the law into your own hands: obtain justice through your own actions instead of going to the police, law courts, etc.   15

leaf, turn over a new leaf: leaf is used here in the old sense of 'page', ie, to start again on a new (clean) page of an exercise book . . .   9

let's face it, . . .: asking the other person to be honest with himself/herself.   18

Unit

let alone: emphatic form of **to say nothing of.**   20

lip service, pay lip service to sg: pretend to agree with or approve of sg without really doing so: *The Government pays lip service to Green issues, but really they don't care at all.*   15

live and let live: be tolerant of other people's behaviour and way of life: *Our new neighbours are very noisy, but we must learn to live and let live.*   13

lock the stable door after the horse has gone/ bolted: (bolted = run away) take action to prevent a problem after the problem has occurred: *You should install a burglar alarm on your house now. It's no use locking the stable door after the horse has gone.* Don't wait until someone breaks into your house before installing an alarm.   17

lose your temper: get angry. Opp, **keep your temper.**   2

loss, be a dead loss: be a complete failure.   11

mad, stark staring mad: stark (= completely) mad with staring eyes.   4

make, not make it: not succeed.   11

meat, one man's meat is another man's poison: not everyone likes the same things.   13

mess, make a mess of sg: do sg very badly. Sim, **make a hash of sg.** *He made a real mess/hash of his maths examination.*   10

milk, it's no use crying over spilt milk: we must not get upset about things which have happened and which we cannot change.   13

mind, give sb a piece of your mind: speak very frankly to sb, tell them exactly what you think of them, cf, **tell sb off, have a go at sb.**   7

mountain, make a mountain out of a molehill: Sim, **make a fuss about nothing:** A mole is a small animal that lives in underground tunnels. As it digs, it throws up the earth, which forms small piles (molehills) above the ground.   9

naked, stark naked: stark emphasises how completely naked you are.   4

neck, stick your neck out: take a chance. Sim, **run/ take a risk:** *You're sticking your neck out if you criticise your boss like that.*   3

needle, needle in a haystack: it would be difficult to find such a small object as a needle in a pile of hay.   8

Unit

nerves, get on your nerves: if sg gets on your nerves, it irritates you. — 1

new, brand new: completely new and unused: *I got a brand new bicycle for my birthday.* — 4

No way!: Strongly emphasising a refusal, denial, etc. — 19

Not a chance!: like **No way!** — 20

not to mention: like **to say nothing of.** — 20

nothing of the sort!: emphasising that what the other person said is completely wrong. — 18

notice, take any notice: usu. negative, *He doesn't take any notice* = He pays no attention. — 2

nowhere, get nowhere fast: make no progress at all. Sim, **to go round in circles:** *I've been working on this essay for hours, but I seem to be getting nowhere fast/going round in circles.* — 11

once and for all: emphasising determination. — 19

or so: or a little bit more. — 20

or something: or something like that. — 18

out of sight, out of mind: you only care about sg while it is present: *'Darling, I shall miss you while you are away'. 'You say that, but I expect it will be a case of out of sight, out of mind.'* — 17

past, wouldn't put it past sb: believe that sb is capable of doing sg bad. — 2

pat, give sb a pat on the back: praise or congratulate sb. Sim, **to pat sb on the back.** — 7

pinch, take it with a pinch of salt: assume that what someone says is exaggerated. — 2

plan, go according to plan: describes something that happened exactly as you wanted it to. *Everything went according to plan on our holiday. Even the sun shone for us.* — 11

play it safe: act cautiously. cf **be on the safe side, look before you leap.** — 3

plunge, take the plunge: do something that requires courage, as in diving into a swimming pool from the diving board. to plunge = to dive. *I didn't know anything about Scotland, but I took the plunge and moved there.* — 3

practise what you preach: behave in the way that you tell other people to behave: *Bill is always talking about the environment, but he throws litter on the ground. He really ought to practise what he preaches.* — 17

Unit

pretty, as pretty as a picture: mostly used to describe people. — 12

problem, No problem!: a short response to a request: *Can you help me mend this table lamp? No problem! I'll be with you in a minute.* — 11

proud, as proud as a peacock: refers to the proud way the male bird displays its magnificent tail feathers. — 12

Put it this way: explaining your idea in another way to make it even clearer. — 18

put the cart before the horse: do things in the wrong order. If you borrow money from the bank to build a garage, and then try to get permission to build the garage, you are putting the cart before (= in front of) the horse. — 17

question, there's no question about it: there is no doubt about sg, it is certain. *There's no question about it: Zambian women are the most beautiful in the world.* Sim, **no two ways about it.** — 6

question, to be out of the question: if sg is out of the question, it will not happen, cannot be done, and there is no point in discussing it any further: *We asked the boss for a rise in salary, but he said that it was out of the question this year.* — 6

red, blood red: *At sunset, the whole sky was blood red.* — 4

right, not be able to do a thing right/wrong: do everything badly/well. — 7

risk, run a risk: take a chance. Sim, **take a risk.** cf, **stick your neck out.** — 3

Rome, when in Rome, do as the Romans do: adapt to different customs when you are in different places. — 9

roof, hit the roof: react angrily to sg. — 2

ropes, know the ropes: Usually referring to your job, the place where you work. The expression comes from sailing and a knowledge of the ropes which control the sails of a ship. — 14

safe, a safe bet: something that is not a risk. cf. **a sure thing:** *Putting money on Argentina to win the football cup was a sure thing. They won 5–0.* — 3

safe, be on the safe side: not take a chance. cf. **play it safe.** *Johnny wanted to go to America, but he didn't have a job there, so he decided to be on the safe side/play it safe and stay in England.* — 3

safe, better to be safe than sorry: prefer not to take a risk/prefer to be safe. — 3

	Unit
think, **think the world of sb:** think very highly of sb.	I

think, **think the world of sb:** think very highly of sb. 　I

thrilled, **thrilled to bits:** very, very pleased/excited about sg: *The children were thrilled to bits with their present.* 　I

thumb, **stand/stick out like a sore thumb:** describes sg or sb that is very noticeable because they are so different from their surroundings. An injured thumb in a bandage is very noticeable: *If you go to the wedding in those old trousers, you will stick out like sore thumb. Everyone else will be dressed up.* 　15

time, **have no time for sb:** to dislike sb, not to want to know sb. Opp: **have a lot of time for sb.** 　I

tired, **dog tired:** very tired. 　4

to say nothing of: adding to a list which is already serious. 　20

toe the line: conform, do what you are told to do (party line = the agreed programme of a political party). 　15

touch, **(a bit) out of touch:** opp. **be/keep/stay in touch:** *I've tried to keep in touch with the latest developments in cancer research.* 　14

two heads are better than one: You will make better decisions if you discuss your problems with others. 　9

upright, **bolt upright:** Used with the verb *sit*: to *sit bolt upright* often suggests a surprised reaction. 　4

walk, **not walk a step:** not move at all. To step is to move forward, putting one foot in front of the other. 　16

way, **go your own way:** Sim, **do your own thing.** 　15

ways, **there are no two ways about it:** emphasising that sg is definitely so: *When the boss says no, there are no two ways about it: he means no!* 　6

wedge, **the thin end of the wedge:** A small beginning can lead to much worse things later. (*wedge* = a triangular block used, eg, to split open a piece of wood.) 　13

wet, **soaking wet:** wet to the skin. 　4

wet blanket: someone who spoils other people's fun in a boring way. 　20

What about ...?: making a suggestion. 　18

	Unit

when it comes to X, . . .: The expression is usually followed by a strong positive or negative statement. 　20

white, **snow white:** as white as snow. 　4

wildfire, **spread like wildfire:** spread very quickly, like a forest fire. 　5

word, **not believe a word of it:** to think a story is untrue. 　2

word, **not breathe a word:** not say anything at all, keep it a secret. Note other expressions on this pattern *NOT VERB A/ANOTHER NOUN* to emphasise: **not sleep a wink, not eat another bite, not sing a note, not understand a word.** 　5

word, **not say a word:** The expression means more than just remain silent. It means not react, not comment. 　2

world, **it takes all sorts to make a world:** be tolerant of people different from yourself. 　9

wrong, **never put a foot wrong:** describes sb who never makes mistakes, always behaves perfectly. 　7

wrong, **not be able to do a thing wrong/right:** do everything perfectly/badly. 　7

Answer key

1 Loving and hating

1

1 Yes, she thinks the world of them.
2 No, she has no time for them.
3 Yes. In fact he's head over heels in love with her.
4 No. In fact he can't stand the sight of her.

2

5 When I was young, I was head over heels in love with the girl next door.
6 I cannot stand [the sight of] good food going to waste.
7 Most of us have no time for people who drink and drive.
8 Our teacher thinks the world of us.

3

9 B   10 A   11 B
12 A   13 B   14 A

4

Suggested answers:
15 It/She drives me up the wall.
It/She gets on my nerves.
16 I was thrilled to bits.
17 It gets on my nerves./It drives me up the wall./I'm sick and tired of it.
18 You have taken a fancy to it.
19 She has a crush on her piano teacher.

5

20 I know that my boyfriend, George, thinks the world of me. We fell head over heels in love the first time we saw each other. My friends said that I had a crush on him, and that it wasn't true love, but I have no time for people who laugh at young love. I'm sick and tired of people telling me 'You're too young to be in love'. They really get on my nerves. It drives me up the wall the way they always think they know best. Anyway, I was thrilled to bits when George asked me to go out with him, and I know that this is the real thing and not just an adolescent fancy.

2 Getting angry and not getting angry; believing and not believing

1

1 Yes, he lost his temper.
2 No, he didn't say a word.
3 Yes, I wouldn't put it past him.
4 No, I don't believe a word of it.

2

5 . . . , but she didn't say a word . . .
6 I don't believe a word of it.
7 I wouldn't put it past them.
8 Try not to lose your temper.

3

9 B   10 A   11 A   12 B
13 B   14 A B   15 B   16 B

4

Suggested answers
17 A likely story!/I don't believe a word of it.
18 I didn't believe a word of it/I didn't believe a word she said/I took it with a pinch of salt.
19 He flew off the handle/He hit the roof.
20 (no surprise) His father didn't bat an eyelid.
(no anger) His father didn't say a word.
21 I couldn't believe my eyes!

5

22 My parents didn't bat an eyelid when I told them I wanted to work in India as a missionary. In fact, my father, instead of hitting the roof as I expected him to, didn't say a word. He just smiled. My mother, who easily loses her temper, also remained calm. In fact, after some discussion, they even offered to pay my air fare: I couldn't believe my ears!
23 A lot of people say that my brother is a liar. Well, I admit he tends to exaggerate, and you have to take everything he says with a pinch of salt, but he doesn't really mean to mislead people. But the problem is that people no longer believe a word he says. Of course I wouldn't put it past him to tell lies if he needed to, but it's a pity he has such a bad name, especially as he is a Member of Parliament.

3 Being safe and taking risks

1

1 Yes, you have to watch your step.
2 He's really sticking his neck out.
3 Well, he likes to be on the safe side.
4 Yes, she decided to take the plunge.

2

5 Sometimes you have to stick your neck out.
6 If you want to succeed in this job, you must always watch your step.
7 She likes to be on the safe side.
8 She took the plunge.

3

9 B   10 A   11 A
12 B   13 B   14 A

4

15 They played it safe.
16 She was running a risk.
17 Keith was skating on thin ice.
18 It's a safe bet.
19 Some people jump in with both feet.
20 It's better to be safe than sorry.

5

21 My two sisters are complete opposites. Mary's very careful about everything. In any situation she likes to be on the safe side. Emily, on the other hand, always jumps in with both feet before she knows the possible problems she might meet. When we all wanted to go on holiday together last year, Mary thought a nice hotel in Spain would be a safe bet, but of course Emily wanted to hitch-hike to India. I didn't like the idea of hitch-hiking – it seemed like running a risk, but I didn't want to play it safe with Mary in her nice hotel either. In the end we did the only thing possible – we all went away separately!

4 Making comparisons which emphasise or exaggerate

1

1 soaking wet
2 wet
3 hungry
4 starving hungry

2

5 blood red
6 brand new
7 crystal clear
8 dirt cheap
9 ice cold
10 pea/sea green
11 razor sharp
12 rock hard
13 sky blue
14 snow white
15 stone deaf
16 wafer thin

3

17 pitch black
18 piping hot
19 soaking wet
20 bone idle
21 stark naked
22 stark staring mad
23 stone cold sober
24 dog tired
25 dead straight
26 bolt upright

4

27 C   28 E   29 F
30 B   31 A   32 D

5 Keeping things quiet and not keeping things quiet

I

1 No, he didn't breathe a word (of it) (to anyone).
2 Yes, I'm afraid he let the cat out of the bag.
3 Oh yes, I'm sure she'll keep it to her herself.
4 No, she's sure to give the game away.

2

5 He'll never give the game away.
6 Keep it to yourself, but . . .
7 I didn't breathe a word.
8 You let the cat out of the bag.

3

9 A   10 B   11 A
12 B   13 A   14 B

4

Suggested answers:
15 My life is an open book.
16 He was a dark horse.
17 The news spread like wildfire.
18 He plays his cards close to his chest/ He's a dark horse.
19 Maria gave the show/game away.
20 He asked me to keep it under my hat.

5

21 not to breathe a word
22 to let the cat out of the bag
23 an open book
24 to keep it under your hat
25 a dark horse
26 to play your cards close to your chest
27 to spread like wildfire

6 Describing certainty and impossibility

I

1 Yes, I think it's on the cards.
2 No, I'm afraid it's out of the question.
3 Yes, it's a sure thing.
4 No, it's a long shot.

2

5 It's quite out of the question.
6 My boss has told me that my promotion is a sure thing.
7 I think it's a long shot.
8 They say rain is on the cards.

3

9 A   10 B   11 A
12 B   13 A   14 B

4

15 There are no two ways about it.
16 It's all very much in the air.
17 It's out of the question.
18 I wouldn't bet on it.
19 I haven't got a cat in Hell's chance.

5

20 When Barry went for an interview for a Manager's job, he thought he didn't have a cat in Hell's chance. His workmates told him that at 23 it was completely out of the question. 'It may be a long shot,' he thought, 'but I'll try anyway.' At the interview, his boss said that his work was good and that a promotion was on the cards. Would he consider a Manager's job? 'You bet!' said Barry. His workmates changed their ideas immediately. 'We always knew it was a sure thing.'

7 Praising and criticising; right and wrong

I

1 Yes, he did, and I gave him a piece of my mind.
2 Yes, she never puts a foot wrong.
3 No, he really put his foot in it.
4 Yes, they all wanted to give her a pat on the back.

2

5 She never puts a foot wrong.
6 They gave Bill a pat on the back.

7 I put my foot in it.
8 He gave me a piece of his mind.

3

9 B   10 A   11 B
12 B   13 A   14 B

4

15 He can't do a thing right.
16 She couldn't do a thing wrong.
17 You're in my good books.
18 Tell him off.
19 He's in her bad books.
20 Don't have a go at me!

5

21 All his life my brother Edward had always been in trouble and couldn't do a thing right. Teachers told him off for being late, for being early, for not being there at all; neighbours gave him a piece of their mind when he played in their gardens and broke their flowers. He was in mother's bad books because he broke all her favourite vases yesterday. But from now on Edward is a star and can't do a thing wrong. The local TV company has just given him the main part in a new children's TV series and now all the teachers, neighbours and family are giving him a big pat on the back. Strange how a little horror can suddenly be in everyone's good books.

8 Making comparisons about states

I

1 Yes, she's like a cat on hot bricks.
2 Absolutely! Talking about Socialism when he's there is like a red rag to a bull.
3 I don't think so . . . it's like looking for a needle in a haystack.
4 Not at all! He's like a bear with a sore head.

2

5 It's like looking for a needle in a haystack.
6 He seems to be like a bear with a sore head.
7 She seems to be like a cat on hot bricks.
8 It's like a red rag to a bull.

3

9 b   10 c   11 d   12 d

4

Suggested answers:
13 He looks like nothing on earth.
14 Her words are 'It's like water off a duck's back.'
15 It went like clockwork.
16 Asking them for money is/It's like trying to get blood out of a stone.

5

17 like looking for a needle in a haystack
18 like water off a duck's back
19 like getting blood out of a stone
20 go like clockwork
21 like a bear with a sore head
22 like a red rag to a bull
23 like a cat on hot bricks
24 like nothing on earth

9 Sayings connected with people's attitudes I

I

1 Well, he always makes a mountain out of a molehill.
2 Believe it or not, he's turned over a new leaf.
3 Not in the least! She always calls a spade a spade.
4 Make sure you dot your i's and cross your t's.

2

5 It's better if they call a spade a spade.
6 He likes to dot his i's and cross his t's.
7 You're really making a mountain out of a molehill.
8 It's about time they turned over a new leaf.

3

9 'If at first you don't succeed, try, try, try again.'
10 'Every cloud has a silver lining.'
11 'Two heads are better than one.'
12 'When in Rome, do as the Romans do.'
13 'It takes all sorts to make a world.'

4

14 Two heads are better than one.
15 When in Rome, do as the Romans do.
16 Every cloud has a silver lining.
17 It takes all sorts to make a world.

5

18 call a spade a spade.
19 turn over a new leaf.
20 two heads are better than one.
21 If at first you don't succeed, try, try, try again.
22 dotting the i's and crossing the t's.
23 make mountains out of molehills.
24 When in Rome, do as the Romans do.
25 Every cloud has a silver lining.
26 It takes all sorts to make a world.

10 Succeeding and not succeeding

I

1 Yes, he's certainly made a good job of it.
2 Oh dear, he's really made a mess of it.
3 Number 6 is streets ahead of everyone.
4 Number 12 is fighting a losing battle.

2

5 He's making a good job of it.
6 He's fighting a losing battle.
7 Everyone knows Porsches are streets ahead of Fords.
8 You often make a mess of things.

3

9 A   10 B   11 B
12 A   13 B   14 A

4

15 The party fell flat.
16 They didn't make a go of it.
17 You know you've made the grade.
18 I'm banging my head against a brick wall.
19 It goes like a bomb.

5

20 My cousin Alfie always wanted to be successful. But he hated school and didn't make a go of it. His friends were always streets ahead of him. He had several jobs and made a mess of all of them. All his plans fell flat. He began to feel he was banging his head against a brick wall. He started to think he would never make the grade in anything. Until one day last year he was offered a job in a circus. Now he is a roaring success. He is the best lion tamer they've ever had!

11 Achieving and not achieving

I

1 I think he's getting to grips with it.
2 In fact, he's getting nowhere fast.
3 Everything went according to plan.
4 No, it was a dead loss.

2

5 Everything went according to plan.
6 All the TV programmes are a dead loss tonight.
7 I'm getting nowhere fast.
8 He's getting to grips with riding his bicycle.

3

9 B   10 A   11 A
12 B   13 B   14 A

4

15 Maria always did her best.
16 It was easier said than done.
17 He went from bad to worse.
18 It was a piece of cake.
19 It's no problem making a promise.
20 People who don't try, don't make it.

5

21 Johnny wanted to earn a lot of money and thought that being a rock star must be a piece of cake. So he and three friends formed a band, learned a few songs and soon made a record which went to Number 2. 'No problem,' they thought, 'from now on.' They made another record but unfortunately this one didn't make it. They made four more which all went nowhere fast. Things went from bad to worse. Soon they had no money and Johnny had to get a job as a cleaner. 'Being a famous rock star,' said Johnny 'is easier said than done.'

12 Making comparisons about people's appearance

I

1 He is as blind as a bat.
2 He is as deaf as a post.
3 He is as bald as a coot.
4 He is as thin as a rake.

2

5 She is as brown as a berry.
6 She is as pretty as a picture.
7 She is as fit as a fiddle.
8 She is as strong as an ox.

3

9 cool – a
10 proud – c
11 sharp – d
12 stubborn – b
13 as stubborn as a mule.
14 as proud as a peacock.
15 as cool as a cucumber.
16 as sharp as a razor.

4

Suggested answers:
17 She feels as proud as a peacock.
18 They stay/remain/are as cool as a cucumber.
19 S/He is as sharp as a razor.
20 She is as stubborn as a mule.

5

21 as bald as a coot
22 as blind as a bat
23 as brown as a berry
24 as deaf as a post
25 as fit as a fiddle
26 as pretty as a picture
27 as strong as an ox
28 as thin as a rake
29 as cool as a cucumber
30 as stubborn as a mule
31 as proud as a peacock
32 as sharp as a razor

13 Sayings connected with people's attitudes 2

1

1 They live and let live.
2 Yes, but it's no use crying over spilt milk.
3 He wants to have his cake and eat it.
4 He's got several irons in the fire.

2

5 He wants to have his cake and eat it.
6 We live and let live.
7 It's no use crying over spilt milk.
8 She's got several irons in the fire.

3

9 it was the last straw.
10 one man's meat is another man's poison.

11 that the first week was (only) the thin end of the wedge.
12 it was like the blind leading the blind.

4

13 One man's meat is another man's poison.
14 It was the thin end of the wedge.
15 It was the last straw (that broke the camel's back).
16 It's like the blind leading the blind.

5

17 Ah well, one man's meat is another man's poison.
18 It's no use crying over spilt milk.
19 It's going to be the blind leading the blind.
20 The trouble with you is you want to have your cake and eat it.

14 Knowing and not knowing

1

1 Yes, he knows all about them.
2 No, he doesn't know the first thing about them.
3 Well, yes, I know a thing or two about them.
4 Me? I can't tell one end of a sports car from the other.
5 Yes. I know this place like the back of my hand.
6 No. I haven't the foggiest idea (where we are).

2

7 He may look stupid, but he knows a thing or two about life.
8 I used to know Madrid like the back of my hand, but it's years since I was last there.
9 I haven't the foggiest idea why there is no butter in the refrigerator.
10 I don't know one end of an electronic keyboard from the other.
11 If you want to know anything about pop music, ask Melanie: she knows all about it.
12 They asked me to write a book on astrophysics. The trouble is, I don't know the first thing about it.

3

| 13 B | 14 A | 15 B |
| 16 A | 17 A | |

4

Suggested answers:
18 I'm a bit out of touch./I haven't a clue what's going on. (emphasising that you don't know anything at all)
19 She knows her subject inside out./ She has the subject at her fingertips.
20 I haven't a clue!
21 The boss's secretary really knows the ropes/knows the job inside out.

5

22 A: How well do you know London?
   B: Like the back of my hand!
   A: Good. So, please tell me where Buckingham Palace is.
   B: I haven't the foggiest idea.
   A: I thought you said you knew this city inside out?
   B: I do, but I haven't got a clue where Buckingham Palace is.
   A: Why not?
   B: I'm a Republican.
23 John is crazy about his new personal computer. He has stored lots of things on it, because, as he says, he likes to have the information at his fingertips. When he first got it, didn't know the first thing about computers (I'm the same: I can't tell one end of a computer from the other). But he soon learned all about them, and now, every day, he sits at his PC hoping that someone will ask him a question!

15 Conforming and not conforming

1

1 He never wants to toe the line.
2 He always wants to do his own thing.
3 No, he only pays lip service (to them).
4 No, she prefers to go her own way.

2

5 He always does his own thing.
6 When you join the army you have to toe the line.
7 I was a secretary for the Nationalist Party, but I only paid lip service to their policies.
8 You always go your own way.

3

| 9 A | 10 B | 11 A |
| 12 B | 13 A | 14 B |

4

15 Rudolf stands out like a sore thumb.
16 She's keeping up with the Joneses.
17 Michael always goes by the book.
18 He's like a fish out of water.
19 You should never take the law into your own hands.
20 Old Fred obeys the letter of the law.

5

21 Albert was a very independent young man who always liked to do his own thing. When he was in the army he hated having to toe the line. He felt like a fish out of water. He refused to go by the book and was always being punished for doing things his own way. The army doesn't like individuals who behave differently from the group and stick out like a sore thumb, and in the end they discharged him. Now he's going his own way. I hear he's travelling around Europe as a pavement artist.

16 Making comparisons about actions

1

1 Yes, she spends money like water.
2 Yes, but they say he hung on like grim death.
3 I know. She smokes like a chimney.
4 Yes, I'm afraid he drinks like a fish.

2

5 Most of us would love a chance to go shopping and spend money like water.
6 Ronald will kill himself if he doesn't stop smoking like a chimney.
7 Vince drank like a fish at the party.
8 Someone tried to steal my mother's handbag, but she hung on to it like grim death.

3

9 He didn't drink a drop.
10 We didn't eat a bite.
11 I mustn't say a/another thing.
12 She can't sing a note.
13 They won't sleep a wink.
14 I can't walk a/another step.

4

15 Oh, no thank you, I couldn't eat a bite.

16 No, I mustn't say a thing.
17 No, I can't walk another step.
18 No, I can't sing a note.
19 No thank you, I couldn't drink another drop.
20 I didn't sleep a wink.

5

21 He didn't sleep a wink.
22 He couldn't eat another bite.
23 He smokes like a chimney.
24 They can't walk another step.
25 He's holding on like grim death.
26 They are not going to say a thing.
27 He can't sing a note.
28 He won't (doesn't) drink a drop.
29 He spends money like water.

17 Sayings connected with people's attitudes 3

1

1 He decided to kill two birds with one stone.
2 Well, I suppose it's better late than never.
3 Yes, I think she's putting the cart before the horse.
4 Yes, great minds think alike.

2

5 He said it was better late than never.
6 Trevor tried to kill two birds with one stone.
7 We say it's because great minds think alike.
8 Buying the furniture before you've got the house is putting the cart before the horse.

3

9 It's out of sight, out of mind.
10 To put locks on the doors after a burglary is to lock the stable door after the horse has gone/bolted.
11 If you agree to do more than you have time for, you are biting off more than you can chew.
12 People like him should practise what they preach.

4

13 He locked the stable door after the horse had gone.
14 She bit off more than she could chew.
15 He should practise what he preaches.
16 Out of sight, out of mind.

5

17 Make sure you don't bite off more than you can chew.
18 Ah, you see, great minds think alike.
19 You ought to practise what you preach.
20 Don't you think that's putting the cart before the horse?
21 You know, out of sight, out of mind.

18 Conversational phrases 1

2

1 Let's face it
2 If you ask me
3 What about
4 or something
5 for a start
6 all very well
7 the fact of the matter is
8 Put it this way
9 Let's face it
10 nothing of the sort
11 It's just that
12 After all
13 at that

3

14 D   15 A   16 B   17 C

4

Suggested answers:
18 What about going to the seaside?
19 Why don't you make yourself a sandwich or something?
20 It's all very well for you. You don't work in a cake shop.
21 He's a bigot, and a racist bigot at that.
22 After all, you started it.
23 For a start, I don't like football.
24 I did/said nothing of the sort!
25 It's just that I don't like the way he always talks to other girls.

19 Conversational phrases 2

2

1 Once and for all
2 anyway
3 I like that!
4 better still
5 No way!
6 In other words

7 in a nutshell
8 Talk about
9 Come on
10 there's no way
11 and that's that
12 That'll be the day!

3

13 C **14** D **15** A **16** B

4

Suggested answers:
17 You can't have either, and that's that.
18 I like that! You smoke much more than I do.
19 Talk about greedy! You've had six already.
20 In other words, we have to stay in.
21 There's no way I want to talk to your mother.
22 In a nutshell, it was the worst and the best time of my life.
23 Better still, I'd love a house with a garden.

20 Conversational phrases 3

2

1 and so on
2 as well
3 To say nothing of
4 a wet blanket
5 not to mention
6 By the way,
7 it's a good job
8 at all
9 Don't change the subject
10 as well as
11 Not a chance!
12 or so
13 or other
14 When it comes to
15 let alone
16 it stands to reason
17 change the subject

3

18 C **19** D **20** A **21** B

4

Suggested answers:
22 We just talked about work, our families, the children and so on.
23 Bring some steaks and sausages, and a bottle of wine as well.
24 Yes. Bring an overcoat as well as a couple of pullovers.
25 The weather was awful and the hotel was terrible, not to mention the delays at the airport.
26 It's a good job I wasn't hungry.
27 I couldn't stand up at the moment let alone climb a hill.
28 It suits you. By the way, what happened to your old dress?
29 I should finish in an hour or so.
30 He wanted/asked for/was looking for some old book or other.
31 I've never been abroad at all.